DREAMLAND

MENTAL MATHEMATICS

BOOK 3

by:

T. Raaj Bhanot

Published by

DREAMLAND PUBLICATIONS

J-128, KIRTI NAGAR, NEW DELHI-110 015 (INDIA)

PHONE : 011- 2510 6050, FAX : 011- 2543 8283

E-mail : dreamland@vsnl.com

Shop online at www.dreamlandpublications.com

Published in 2015 by
Dreamland Publications
J-128, Kirti Nagar, New Delhi- 110 015 (India)
Tel.: 011-2510 6050, Fax : 011-2543 8283

ISBN 978-93-5089-190-2

PREFACE

The present series—DREAMLAND'S GRADED MENTAL MATHEMATICS—aims at serving as an active guide to teachers and students for acquiring quick methods of calculations. The methods are bound to be useful not only during the school-stage but in practical life also when the students have grown up to enter life.

The handy tips about calculations are sure to sharpen the intellectual capacity of the learners—a capacity that is a must in the fast-changing life-styles of today. Men with sharp brain are in high demand almost in every walk of life. Tough competition in every field calls for brain with brawn indeed.

The present book is meant for children of age-group 8+ which corresponds to standard III of the primary schools. It deals with—

- 4-Digit Numerals along with their Numeration and Notation as well as Place Value.

- Various methods and skills in basic four operations— Addition, Subtraction, Multiplication and Division.

- Simple Fractions with two basic operations—Addition and Subtraction.

- Concepts of Equivalent Fractions, Like Fractions and Unlike Fractions.

- Some Miscellaneous Skills in Multiplication, Division and Squaring.

- Some Concepts of Geometry—Vertices, Diagonals and Perimeter.

We feel highly delighted while placing this series in the hands of the teachers and the taught with a positive hope that it will meet their approval admirably. It is certainly a series with a difference. As no human work can claim to be flawless, constructive suggestions for the betterment of the series shall be welcomed to be incorporated in the coming editions if found up to the mark.

—PUBLISHERS

CONTENTS

① WHAT WE ALREADY KNOW

A. Fill up each blank :

1. The left-end digit in a 3-digit numeral shows _Hundreds_ .

2. The middle digit in a 3-digit numeral shows _Tens_ .

3. The right-end digit in a 3-digit numeral shows _Ones_ .

4. The highest 3-digit numeral is _999_ .

5. The lowest 3-digit numeral is _100_ .

6. We can form a _3 digit_ number using any 3-digits.

7. Numerals written from the lowest to the highest are in _ascending_ order.

8. Numerals written from the highest to the lowest are in _descending_ order.

9. A prime number can be divided by _itself_ and 1 only.

10. 2, 3, 4 and 7 are four _____ digits but 1 is not.

11. Multiplication means _adding_ a number to itself many times.

12. A square has all its sides as well as _____ equal.

13. All the four angles of a rectangle are _____ angles.

14. An angle of 180° is called a _____ angle.

15. An angle of 360° is called a _____ .

B. Write the correct numeral in each blank :

1. _10_ tens make a hundred.

2. _10_ ones make a ten.

3. We write a hundred using _3_ digits.

4. There are _____ prime numerals from 1 to 100.

5. The result of multiplication is called _product_ .

6. A numeral that divides another numeral is called its _divisor_ .

C. Write the correct product in each blank :

◻ 9 times 2 = _____   ◻ 7 times 3 = _____

◻ 8 times 4 = _____   ◻ 5 times 5 = _____

◻ 4 times 6 = _____   ◻ 3 times 9 = _____

◻ 2 times 8 = _____   ◻ 10 times 10 = _____

D. Answer :

◻ How many sides bound a triangle ?   _____

◻ What is a triangle with one right angle called ?   _____

◻ Is an obtuse angle larger than 180° ?   _____

◻ Which triangle has all its angles equal ?   _____

◻ Which triangle has two of its sides equal ?   _____

◻ How many sides bound a quadrilateral ?   _____

E. Name each figure shown below :

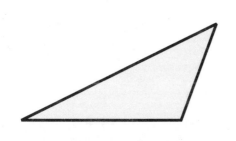

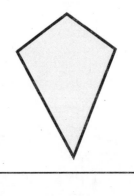

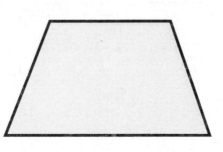

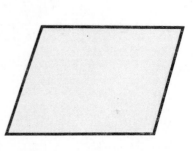

② 4-DIGIT NUMERALS

- 10 ones make a **ten**.

- 10 tens make a **hundred**.

- 9 hundreds and 99 make **999**.

- 10 hundreds make a thousand.

- We write a thousand using 4 digits.

THOUSANDS	HUNDREDS	TENS	ONES
1	0	0	0

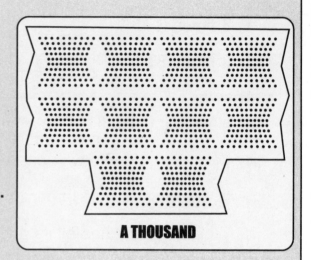

A THOUSAND

DO YOURSELF

A. Write the **correct numeral** in each box :

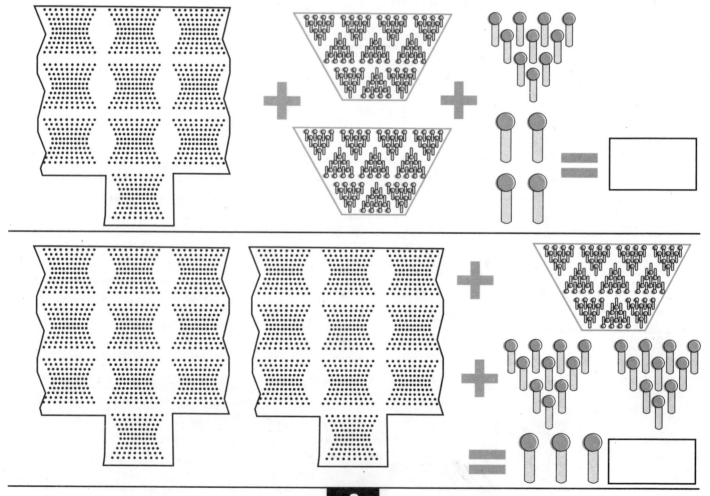

B. Write in each box, the :

☐ lowest 1-digit numeral = _____   ☐ highest 1-digit numeral = _____

☐ lowest 2-digit numeral = _____   ☐ highest 2-digit numeral = _____

☐ lowest 3-digit numeral = _____   ☐ highest 3-digit numeral = _____

☐ lowest 4-digit numeral = _____   ☐ highest 4-digit numeral = _____

C. Write the **correct numeral** in each blank :

☐ Three thousand six hundred and thirty-five _____

☐ Five thousand four hundred and fifty-seven _____

☐ Seven thousand eight hundred and twenty-nine _____

☐ Eight thousand seven hundred and sixty-four _____

☐ Two thousand 3 hundred and seventy-six _____

☐ One thousand nine hundred and eighty-nine _____

☐ Four thousand five hundred and forty-seven _____

☐ Six thousand seven hundred and ninety-eight _____

D. Write each **numeral** in words :

☐ 7453 = _____

☐ 9507 = _____

☐ 3876 = _____

☐ 8236 = _____

☐ 2909 = _____

☐ 5468 = _____

☐ 6795 = _____

☐ 4729 = _____

☐ 7390 = _____

☐ 1003 = _____

③ FORMING 4-DIGIT NUMERALS

- If we are to form all possible numerals using the digit 1, 2, 3, 4, we shall place **1 in the thousand's place** and the other digits as **hundreds**, **tens** and **ones** in turn to form 6 numerals.

  We shall repeat this process with **2 in the thousand's place**.

  We shall repeat again the process with **3 in the thousand's place**.

  We shall repeat once again the process with 4 **in the thousand's place**.

1234	1243	1324
1342	1423	1432
2134	2143	2324
2334	2423	2432
3124	3142	3214
3241	3412	3421
4123	4132	4713
4231	4312	4321

- Thus we shall form 24 numerals in all.
- To form the lowest numeral, write the digits in **ascending** order, *i.e.* 1234.
- To form the highest numeral, write the digits in descending order, *i.e.* 4321.

DO YOURSELF

A. Form the **24 possible numerals** with the digits **5, 6, 7, 8** :

B. Write the **lowest** and the **highest** numerals formed with each set of digits :

		Lowest	Highest
❏	2, 4, 6, 8		
❏	3, 5, 7, 9		
❏	0, 1, 3, 5		
❏	2, 6, 9, 7		
❏	3, 6, 8, 9		
❏	5, 4, 3, 2		
❏	3, 2, 1, 0		
❏	6, 5, 4, 3		
❏	5, 3, 4, 0		

C. Write the—

❏ smallest 4-digit numeral : _____

❏ highest 4-digit numeral : _____

❏ number of tens in the highest 4-digit numeral : _____

❏ number ones in the highest 4-digit numeral : _____

❏ number of hundreds in the highest 4-digit numeral : _____

❏ number of ones in the lowest 4-digit numeral : _____

❏ number of tens in the lowest 4-digit numeral : _____

❏ number of hundreds in the lowest 4-digit numeral : _____

❏ difference between the highest and the lowest 4-digit numerals : _____

❏ sum of the highest and the lowest 4-digit numerals : _____

4 WRITING NUMERALS AS NUMBERS

- Write the

  ☐ fourth digit from the right as thousands.

  ☐ third digit from the right as hundreds.

  ☐ second digit from the right as tens.

  ☐ first digit from the right as ones.

9453
= Nine thousands +
four hundreds +
five tens   +
three ones   +

Nine thousand four hundred and fifty-three.

DO YOURSELF

A. Write in words :

☐ 5934 = Five thousand nine hundred and thirty-four.

☐ 5839 = _____

☐ 9299 = _____

☐ 5451 = _____

☐ 3802 = _____

☐ 8202 = _____

☐ 3447 = _____

☐ 9345 = _____

☐ 4963 = _____

☐ 7382 = _____

☐ 5327 = _____

B. Tick (✓) the **correct number** for each numeral :

☐ 5070 } = Five thousand and seventy. ▢
         = Fifty hundred and seventy. ▢

☐ 8166 } = Eight thousand six hundred and sixteen. ▢
         = Eight thousand one hundred and sixty-six. ▢

☐ 4535 } = Four thousand four hundred forty-five. ▢
         = Four thousand five hundred and thirty-five. ▢

☐ 4544 } = Four thousand four hundred forty-five. ▢
         = Four thousand five hundred and forty-four. ▢

☐ 7332 } = Seven thousand three hundred and thirty-two. ▢
         = Seven thousand two hundred and thirty-three. ▢

☐ 5853 } = Five thousand eight hundred and thirty-five. ▢
         = Five thousand eight hundred and fifty-three. ▢

☐ 6523 } = Six thousand five hundred and twenty-three. ▢
         = Six thousand five hundred and thirty-two. ▢

☐ 9345 } = Nine thousand three hundred and fifty-four. ▢
         = Nine thousand three hundred and forty-five. ▢

☐ 8395 } = Eight thousand three hundred and ninety-five. ▢
         = Eight thousand nine hundred and fifty-three. ▢

C. Complete each **number-name** :

☐ 6732 = _____ thousand _____ hundred and _____ -two.

☐ 4641 = Four _____ six _____ and forty - _____ .

☐ 9342 = _____ thousand _____ hundred and _____ .

☐ 8517 = Eight _____ five _____ and _____

☐ 3830 = _____ thousand _____ hundred and _____ .

☐ 8535 = Eight _____ five _____ and _____-five.

☐ 9745 = _____ thousand _____ hundred and _____ .

5 PREDECESSOR AND SUCCESSOR

READ CAREFULLY

- The word—**predecessor**—comes from the verb—precede.
- **Precede** means to come before.
- So a predecessor is the number or numeral that comes just before a given number.
- The word—**successor**—comes from the verb—succeed.
- Succeed means to come after.
- So a successor is the number or numeral that comes just after a given number.

PREDECESSOR

= the given number −1 ; as :

Predecessor of 4095 =

4095 − 1 = 4094

*****

SUCCESSOR

= the given number + 1 ; as

Successor of 4095 =

4095 + 1 = 4096

DO YOURSELF

A. Write the **predecessor** and the **successor** :

☐	← 4721 →	
☐	← 3332 →	
☐	← 7863 →	
☐	← 8919 →	
☐	← 3831 →	
☐	← 3161 →	
☐	← 5813 →	
☐	← 3185 →	

B. Write the numeral between the predecessor and successor :

Predecessor	Numeral	Successor
☐ 2418	_____	2420
☐ 2644	_____	2646
☐ 4812	_____	4814
☐ 3828	_____	3830
☐ 6266	_____	6268
☐ 7829	_____	7831
☐ 3670	_____	3672

C. Fill up the correct numeral in each blank :

Predecessor	Numeral	Successor
☐ 2314	_____	_____
☐ _____	3442	_____
☐ _____	_____	6466
☐ 3670	_____	3672
☐ _____	4455	_____
☐ _____	_____	3381

D. Write the words predecessor and successor where suitable :

[_____]

[_____]

[_____]

⑥ PLACE VALUE

- In the numeral **3247**—

  ☐ 3 is in the **thousand's place.**
  So its place value] = 3000

  ☐ 2 is in the **hundred's place.**
  So its place value] = 200

  ☐ 4 is in the **ten's place.**
  So its place value] = 40

  ☐ 7 is in the **one's place.**
  So its place value] = 7

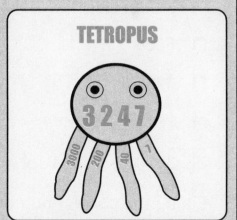

TETROPUS

DO YOURSELF

A. Write the place value of the **ringed digit** :

Numeral	Place Values	Numeral	Place Values
☐ 7 1 ⑧ 3	_____	② 4 9 7	_____
☐ 9 1 3 ⑤	_____	5 3 ⑥ 4	_____
☐ 6 ③ 2 0	_____	4 ⑨ 2 7	_____
☐ ④ 5 6 3	_____	6 5 3 ④	_____

B. Write the place values of the **ringed digits** :

- ☐ ⑤ 6 3 ④ _____ and _____
- ☐ 2 ⑦ ① 8 _____ and _____
- ☐ ⑤ 7 ⑨ 1 _____ and _____
- ☐ 4 ③ 5 ② _____ and _____

❏ ⑤3 7⑧ _____ and _____

❏ 6①6⓪ _____ and _____

C. Write each number as a **numeral** :

❏ Five thousand seven hundred and ninety-one _____

❏ Six thousand one hundred and fifty-nine. _____

❏ Four thousand three hundred and fifty-two. _____

❏ Two thousand eight hundred and thirty-four. _____

❏ Nine thousand one hundred and fifty-seven. _____

❏ Three thousand eight hundred and thirty-two. _____

❏ Eight thousand four hundred twenty-three. _____

❏ Eight thousand six hundred and thirty-one. _____

❏ Seven thousand two hundred and thirty-three. _____

❏ Nine thousand five hundred and sixty-three. _____

D. Write which **numeral** am I, if :

❏ 3139 is my successor ?

❏ 8351 is my predecessor ?

❏ I am 100 less than 9837 ?

❏ I am 1000 more than 8547 ?

❏ I come between 8320 and 8322 ?

❏ I precede the highest 4 digit number ?

❏ I succeed the lowest 4-digit number ?

❏ I am the highest number formed by digits 3, 4, 7, 9 ?

❏ I am the lowest number formed by digits 8, 5, 1, 6 ?

COMPARING NUMERALS

- Comparing numerals means to find out which numeral is higher and which lower.

- Observe the left-hand digits of the numerals.

- The numeral with higher digit at the left end is the higher.

- If the left-hand digit is the same, compare the next digits.

- The process can be continued, if the next digits are also the same.

5543 > 3572 because 5 > 3

5437 > 5271 because digit 5 is the same but the second digit 4 > second digit 2.

5537 > 5526 because its digits 5, 5 are the same but the third digit 3 > third digit 2.

DO YOURSELF

A. Put the sign > or < in each box :

☐ 6325		5583	☐ 8328		9318
☐ 9651		3362	☐ 6214		6606
☐ 4272		4725	☐ 4445		3463
☐ 7705		6702	☐ 3328		4293
☐ 6325		8231	☐ 7391		8321

B. Put the sign < or > in each box :

☐ 4723		4675	☐ 2785		2832
☐ 6066		6237	☐ 4035		4047
☐ 4226		4247	☐ 6325		6383

☐ 4136 [ ] 2226   ☐ 4326 [ ] 4329

☐ 5830 [ ] 5857   ☐ 8325 [ ] 8367

C. Write in the ascending order using the sign (<) :

☐ 2675, 2876, 2756, 2856

_____ < _____ < _____ < _____

☐ 4327, 4587, 4230, 4136

_____ < _____ < _____ < _____

☐ 3532, 3704, 3463, 3715, 3627

_____ < _____ < _____ < _____

☐ 5269, 5312, 5352, 52,48

_____ < _____ < _____ < _____

☐ 7893, 7599, 7312, 7486

_____ < _____ < _____ < _____

☐ 1423, 1253, 1249, 1466

_____ < _____ < _____ < _____

C. Write in the descending order using the sign of (>)

☐ 3569, 3817, 3673, 3264

_____ > _____ > _____ > _____

☐ 2354, 2465, 2265, 2479

_____ > _____ > _____ > _____

☐ 8851, 8408, 8576, 8789

_____ > _____ > _____ > _____

☐ 5519, 5275, 5576, 5248

_____ > _____ > _____ > _____

☐ 4322, 4476, 4359, 4467

_____ > _____ > _____ > _____

8 ADDITION OF DOUBLES

READ CAREFULLY

- In the given numeral—
  - ▢ Pin-point the double digits.
  - ▢ Separate them and then add to find the sum.

$2516 + 6$
$= 2510 + 6 + 6$
$= 2510 + 12 = 2522$

DO YOURSELF

A. **Add mentally :**

▢ $2709 + 9$
$= 2700 + 9 + 9 = 2700 + 18 = \boxed{2718}$

▢ $4608 + 8$
= _____ + _____ + _____ = _____ + _____ = ☐

▢ $3257 + 7$
= _____ + _____ + _____ = _____ + _____ = ☐

▢ $2417 + 7$
= _____ + _____ + _____ = _____ + _____ = ☐

▢ $1734 + 34$
= _____ + _____ + _____ = _____ + _____ = ☐

▢ $7525 + 25$
= _____ + _____ + _____ = _____ + _____ = ☐

▢ $1718 + 18$
= _____ + _____ + _____ = _____ + _____ = ☐

▢ $8912 + 12$
= _____ + _____ + _____ = _____ + _____ = ☐

B. Solve the problems **mentally** :

❑ A cart had 8218 melons on it. 18 more melons were placed on it. How many melons had the cart got in all ?

= _____ + _____ + _____ = _____ + _____ = [ ]

❑ There were 1427 students in a school. 7 more students got admitted in the school. How many students had the school got in all ?

= _____ + _____ + _____ = _____ + _____ = [ ]

❑ There were 3589 soldiers in a fort. 9 more soldiers came there. How many soldiers were there in the fort in all ?

= _____ + _____ + _____ = _____ + _____ = [ ]

❑ A garden had 7725 trees. 25 more trees were planted in it. Find the total number of trees in the garden.

= _____ + _____ + _____ = _____ + _____ = [ ]

❑ There are 9921 buses plying in a town. 21 more buses are bought. How many buses has the town got now ?

= _____ + _____ + _____ = _____ + _____ = [ ]

❑ A company had 4315 workers in it. 15 more workers were employed in the company. How many workers had the company in all ?

= _____ + _____ + _____ = _____ + _____ = [ ]

❑ A small village had 9915 people living in it. 15 more people came to this village. How many people had the village in all ?

= _____ + _____ + _____ = _____ + _____ = [ ]

❑ A railway train had 7623 passengers at a station. 23 new passengers boarded the train here. Find the total number of passengers in the train.

= _____ + _____ + _____ = _____ + _____ = [ ]

❑ A herd has 1724 cattle. 24 more cattle join the herd. Find the total number of cattle in the herd.

= _____ + _____ + _____ = _____ + _____ = [ ]

❑ A flock of sheep had 2516 sheep in it. 16 more sheep joined the flock. How many sheep had the flock got in all ?

= _____ + _____ + _____ = _____ + _____ = [ ]

9 ADDITION BY ROUNDING NUMERALS—I

- Round up one of the numerals to the nearest thousand.
- Then subtract the digit used for rounding the numeral.

$$2845 + 999$$
$$= 2845 + 1000 - 1$$
$$= 3845 - 1 = 3844$$
$$2845 + 999 = 3844$$

DO YOURSELF

A. Add by rounding the numerals :

❑ 2743 + 999

2743 + 1000 − 1 = 3743 − 1 = $\boxed{3742}$

❑ 3683 + 999

= _____ + _____ − _____ = _____ − _____ = ☐

❑ 4528 + 998

= _____ + _____ − _____ = _____ − _____ = ☐

❑ 4372 + 997

= _____ + _____ − _____ = _____ − _____ = ☐

❑ 4298 + 996

= _____ + _____ − _____ = _____ − _____ = ☐

❑ 8725 + 995

= _____ + _____ − _____ = _____ − _____ = ☐

❑ 8517 + 992

= _____ + _____ − _____ = _____ − _____ = ☐

❑ 5348 + 994

= _____ + _____ − _____ = _____ − _____ = ☐

B. **Solve these problems mentally :**

☐ A regiment had 4528 soldiers. 999 more soldiers joined the regiment. Find the total number of soldiers in the regiment.

= _____ + _____ – _____ = _____ – _____ = [   ]

☐ A garden had 8423 trees in it. 997 more trees were planted in it. How many trees were there in the garden in all ?

= _____ + _____ – _____ = _____ – _____ = [   ]

☐ There were 1663 workers in a factory. 995 more workers were employed in it. Now many workers were there in the factory in all ?

= _____ + _____ – _____ = _____ – _____ = [   ]

☐ The police force of a city has 3587 policemen. 998 more policemen are enlisted in the force. What is the strength of the police force now ?

= _____ + _____ – _____ = _____ – _____ = [   ]

☐ A village has a population of 6244 people. 994 children were born in the village in ten years. What is the new population of the village ?

= _____ + _____ – _____ = _____ – _____ = [   ]

☐ A secondary school has 1121 students on 31st of March. Its primary branches have 999 students. What is the total strength of the school ?

= _____ + _____ – _____ = _____ – _____ = [   ]

☐ 4298 labourers were engaged to dig a canal by a contractor. 996 more labourers had to be engaged to complete the work in time. How many labourers were at work in all ?

= _____ + _____ – _____ = _____ – _____ = [   ]

☐ 8172 spectators sat in a stadium to see a cricket match at first. 997 more spectators reached there. How many spectators were in the stadium in all ?

= _____ + _____ – _____ = _____ – _____ = [   ]

☐ 9142 pilgrims set out to visit a shrine. 993 more pilgrims joined them on the way. Find the total number of the pilgrims.

= _____ + _____ – _____ = _____ – _____ = [   ]

☐ A cart has 9216 watermelons loaded in it. 993 more watermelons have been loaded on it. Find the total number of watermelons on the cart.

= _____ + _____ – _____ = _____ – _____ = [   ]

READ CAREFULLY

- Round off one of the numerals to the nearest hundred.

- Add the numerals.

- Subtract the numerals added for rounding the numeral from the total to get the sum.

$$4269 + 248$$
$$= 4269 + 300 - 52$$
$$= 4569 - 52$$
$$= 4517$$

$$4269 + 248 = 4517$$

DO YOURSELF

A. Add by rounding the numerals :

❏ $4227 + 179$
$= 4227 + 200 - 21 = 4427 - 21 = \boxed{4406}$

❏ $6942 + 284$

= _____ + _____ − _____ = _____ − _____ = [   ]

❏ $2132 + 467$

= _____ + _____ − _____ = _____ − _____ = [   ]

❏ $3750 + 892$

= _____ + _____ − _____ = _____ − _____ = [   ]

❏ $3633 + 175$

= _____ + _____ − _____ = _____ − _____ = [   ]

❏ $8266 + 472$

= _____ + _____ − _____ = _____ − _____ = [   ]

❏ $6187 + 684$

= _____ + _____ − _____ = _____ − _____ = [   ]

B. Solve these problems **mentally** :

☐ A school library has 2596 English books and 563 Hindi books. How many books there in the library in all ?

= _____ + _____ − _____ = _____ − _____ = [   ]

☐ A state has 4985 primary school and 385 secondary schools. Find the total number of schools in the state.

= _____ + _____ − _____ = _____ − _____ = [   ]

☐ 8954 people visited the Red Fort on Sunday. But on Monday only 495 people visited it due to rain. Find the total number of people who visited the Red Fort.

= _____ + _____ − _____ = _____ − _____ = [   ]

☐ Bess collected 8789 stamps in a year. But Mary could collect only 747 stamps. How many stamps did both the sisters collect in all ?

= _____ + _____ − _____ = _____ − _____ = [   ]

☐ A father earns Rs. 6560 in a month. But his son earns only Rs. 394 in a month. What is their total monthly income ?

= _____ + _____ − _____ = _____ − _____ = [   ]

☐ The population of a town is 9394 while a small extension of that town has only 488 people living in it. Find the total population of the town.

= _____ + _____ − _____ = _____ − _____ = [   ]

☐ A town has 6936 literate adults living in it. 783 children are yet in schools. Find the total number of literates in the town.

= _____ + _____ − _____ = _____ − _____ = [   ]

☐ There are 6066 one-rupee coins in a bag. Besides there are 267 five-rupee coins also in it. Find the total number of coins in the bag.

= _____ + _____ − _____ = _____ − _____ = [   ]

☐ A printer costs Rs 6647 while a mouse costs only Rs. 760. Find the total cost of both in rupees.

= _____ + _____ − _____ = _____ − _____ = [   ]

☐ A man bought a cycle for Rs. 4986 and a mouth-organ for Rs. 485. How much money did he spend in all ?

= _____ + _____ − _____ = _____ − _____ = [   ]

11 ADDING A STRING OF NUMERALS

READ CAREFULLY

- Group the numerals in pairs such that they can make the nearest tens, twenties, thirties, etc.

- Then add each pair to get these tens, twenties or thirties.

- Finally add the totals to get the sum.

$$209 + 102 + 201 + 108$$
$$= (209 + 201) + (102 + 108)$$
$$= 410 + 210 = 620$$

$$209 + 102 + 201 + 108 = 620$$

DO YOURSELF

A. Do these sums by grouping :

❐ $102 + 103 + 106 + 108 + 114 + 107$

$= (102 + 108) + (103 + 107) + (106 + 114) = 210 + 210 + 220 = \boxed{640}$

❐ $613 + 114 + 107 + 256 + 206 + 104$

$= (\underline{\quad} + \underline{\quad}) + (\underline{\quad} + \underline{\quad}) + (\underline{\quad} + \underline{\quad}) = \underline{\quad} + \underline{\quad} + \underline{\quad} = \boxed{}$

❐ $122 + 404 + 165 + 208 + 106 + 205$

$= (\underline{\quad} + \underline{\quad}) + (\underline{\quad} + \underline{\quad}) + (\underline{\quad} + \underline{\quad}) = \underline{\quad} + \underline{\quad} + \underline{\quad} = \boxed{}$

❐ $215 + 126 + 104 + 303 + 207 + 205$

$= (\underline{\quad} + \underline{\quad}) + (\underline{\quad} + \underline{\quad}) + (\underline{\quad} + \underline{\quad}) = \underline{\quad} + \underline{\quad} + \underline{\quad} = \boxed{}$

❐ $227 + 426 + 134 + 103 + 406 + 204$

$= (\underline{\quad} + \underline{\quad}) + (\underline{\quad} + \underline{\quad}) + (\underline{\quad} + \underline{\quad}) = \underline{\quad} + \underline{\quad} + \underline{\quad} = \boxed{}$

❐ $443 + 219 + 201 + 207 + 227 + 203$

$= (\underline{\quad} + \underline{\quad}) + (\underline{\quad} + \underline{\quad}) + (\underline{\quad} + \underline{\quad}) = \underline{\quad} + \underline{\quad} + \underline{\quad} = \boxed{}$

❐ $216 + 301 + 312 + 109 + 214 + 8$

$= (\underline{\quad} + \underline{\quad}) + (\underline{\quad} + \underline{\quad}) + (\underline{\quad} + \underline{\quad}) = \underline{\quad} + \underline{\quad} + \underline{\quad} = \boxed{}$

12 SUBTRACTION USING PLACE VALUES

READ CAREFULLY

- Write the place values of the digits of the numerals.

- Then subtract the corresponding place values.

- Finally write the remainder according to the resulting place values.

$9278 - 47$

$= 9000 + 200 + 70 + 8 - 40 - 7$

$= 9000 + 200 + 30 + 1 = 9231$

$9278 - 47 = 9231$

DO YOURSELF

A. Do these sums by **place values** :

- 2579 – 45
= 2000 + 500 + 70 + 9 – 40 – 5
= 2000 + 500 + 30 + 4 = $\boxed{2534}$

- 6897 – 76

= ____ + ____ + ___ + ___ – ___ – ___ = ____ + ___ + ___ + ___ = $\boxed{}$

- 7457 – 35

= ____ + ____ + ___ + ___ – ___ – ___ = ____ + ___ + ___ + ___ = $\boxed{}$

- 2897 – 84

= ____ + ____ + ___ + ___ – ___ – ___ = ____ + ___ + ___ + ___ = $\boxed{}$

- 3998 – 75

= ____ + ____ + ___ + ___ – ___ – ___ = ____ + ___ + ___ + ___ = $\boxed{}$

- 6474 – 63

= ____ + ____ + ___ + ___ – ___ – ___ = ____ + ___ + ___ + ___ = $\boxed{}$

- 5277 – 45

= ____ + ____ + ___ + ___ – ___ – ___ = ____ + ___ + ___ + ___ = $\boxed{}$

- 7257 – 35

= ____ + ____ + ___ + ___ – ___ – ___ = ____ + ___ + ___ + ___ = $\boxed{}$

13 SUBTRACTION OF DOUBLES

- In the given numeral—
- Pin-point the double digits.
- Separate them and then subtract the remainder.

$5324 - 12$

$= 5300 + 24 - 12$

$= 5300 + 12 = 5312$

$5324 - 12 + 5312$

DO YOURSELF

A. Subtract mentally :

❏ $6422 - 11$

$= 6422 - 11 = 6400 + 22 - 11 = 6400 + 11 = \boxed{6411}$

❏ $6874 - 37$

= _____ – ____ = _____ + _____ – ____ = _____ + _____ = ☐

❏ $6874 - 37$

= _____ – ____ = _____ + _____ – ____ = _____ + _____ = ☐

❏ $6244 - 22$

= _____ – ____ = _____ + _____ – ____ = _____ + _____ = ☐

❏ $3556 - 28$

= _____ – ____ = _____ + _____ – ____ = _____ + _____ = ☐

❏ $8238 - 19$

= _____ – ____ = _____ + _____ – ____ = _____ + _____ = ☐

❏ $9484 - 42$

= _____ – ____ = _____ + _____ – ____ = _____ + _____ = ☐

❏ $5764 - 32$

= _____ – ____ = _____ + _____ – ____ = _____ + _____ = ☐

❏ $6536 - 18$

= _____ – ____ = _____ + _____ – ____ = _____ + _____ = ☐

B. Subtract mentally :

☐ There were 6286 students in a school. 43 students left the school. How many students were left behind ?

= _____ – ____ = _____ + _____ – ____ = _____ + _____ = [ ]

☐ There were 1764 soldiers in a fort. 32 soldiers were killed in a battle. How many soldiers were left behind ?

= _____ – ____ = _____ + _____ – ____ = _____ + _____ = [ ]

☐ A cart had 7782 melons on it. 41 melons rolled off the cart. How many melons were left behind on the cart ?

= _____ – ____ = _____ + _____ – ____ = _____ + _____ = [ ]

☐ A garden had 7458 trees in it. 29 trees got uprooted in a storm. How many trees were left behind in the garden ?

= _____ – ____ = _____ + _____ – ____ = _____ + _____ = [ ]

☐ A small village had 3968 people living in it. 34 people left the village forever. How many people were left behind in the village ?

= _____ – ____ = _____ + _____ – ____ = _____ + _____ = [ ]

☐ A herd has 6274 cattle. 37 cattle are sold off by the herdsman. How many cattle were left in the herd ?

= _____ – ____ = _____ + _____ – ____ = _____ + _____ = [ ]

☐ A factory has 2884 workers in it. 42 workers were dismissed out of them. How many workers has the factory got now ?

= _____ – ____ = _____ + _____ – ____ = _____ + _____ = [ ]

☐ A railway train has 9272 passengers. 36 passengers got down from the train. How many passengers are there in the train now ?

= _____ – ____ = _____ + _____ – ____ = _____ + _____ = [ ]

☐ A flock has 7456 sheep in it. 28 sheep fall ill and die. How many sheep are left behind in the flock ?

= _____ – ____ = _____ + _____ – ____ = _____ + _____ = [ ]

☐ 1848 buses are plying on the roads of a town. 24 buses break down and are not road-worthy. How many good buses are plying on the town's roads now ?

= _____ – ____ = _____ + _____ – ____ = _____ + _____ = [ ]

14 SUBTRACTION OF NEAR DOUBLES

READ CAREFULLY

- Add a digit to the higher numeral to make its two right-hand digits the same as of the numeral to be subtracted.
- Then subtract the numeral as well as the added digit to get the remainder.

$$2449 - 51$$
$$= 2451 - 51 - 2$$
$$= 2400 - 2 = 2398$$
$$2449 - 51 = 2398$$

DO YOURSELF

A. Subtract **mentally** :

☐ 6418 – 19
   = 6819 – 19 – 1 = 6800 – 1 = **6799**

☐ 5615 – 16

= _____ – _____ – _____ = _____ – _____ = [   ]

☐ 2455 – 57

= _____ – _____ – _____ = _____ – _____ = [   ]

☐ 8427 – 28

= _____ – _____ – _____ = _____ – _____ = [   ]

☐ 9840 – 42

= _____ – _____ – _____ = _____ – _____ = [   ]

☐ 9327 – 29

= _____ – _____ – _____ = _____ – _____ = [   ]

☐ 6335 – 37

= _____ – _____ – _____ = _____ – _____ = [   ]

☐ 7322 – 24

= _____ – _____ – _____ = _____ – _____ = [   ]

☐ 6536 – 38

= _____ – _____ – _____ = _____ – _____ = [   ]

B. Subtract **mentally** :

☐ A railway train had 6837 passengers at a station. 38 passengers got down there. How many passengers were left behind ?

= _____ – ____ = _____ – ____ – ____ = _____ – ___ = [   ]

☐ A small village has a population of 7856 people. 58 people leave the village for work in a town. How many people are there in the village now ?

= _____ – ____ = _____ – ____ – ____ = _____ – ___ = [   ]

☐ A fleet of 6269 buses are plying on the roads of a city. 70 buses get out of order and are not road-worthy. How many buses are plying in the city now ?

= _____ – ____ = _____ – ____ – ____ = _____ – ___ = [   ]

☐ A cart has 5349 melons loaded on it. 50 melons roll off the cart. How many melons are there on the cart now ?

= _____ – ____ = _____ – ____ – ____ = _____ – ___ = [   ]

☐ There were 7129 students in a school. 32 students left the school due to transfers of their fathers. How many students were left behind in the school ?

= _____ – ____ = _____ – ____ – ____ = _____ – ___ = [   ]

☐ A garden had 2126 trees planted in rows. 27 trees were uprooted in a storm. How many trees were left behind in the garden ?

= _____ – ____ = _____ – ____ – ____ = _____ – ___ = [   ]

☐ A factory has 2884 workers in it. 42 workers were dismissed out of them. How many workers has the factory got now ?

= _____ – ____ = _____ – ____ – ____ = _____ – ___ = [   ]

☐ A herd had 6476 cattle. 78 cattle were sold off by the owner. How many cattle were left behind in the herd ?

= _____ – ____ = _____ – ____ – ____ = _____ – ___ = [   ]

☐ There were 9388 workers in a mill. 90 workers were dismissed from service. How many workers were left behind in the mill ?

= _____ – ____ = _____ – ____ – ____ = _____ – ___ = [   ]

☐ A flock has 8434 sheep in it. 35 sheep are sold off to another shepherd. How many sheep has the flock got now ?

= _____ – ____ = _____ – ____ – ____ = _____ – ___ = [   ]

15 SUBTRACTION BY ROUNDING NUMERALS—I

- Round off the numeral to be subtracted to the nearest **thousand** by adding a digit to it.
- Subtract the thousand from the higher numeral.

3032–999

= **3032–1000+1**

= **2032+1 = 2033**

3032 – 999 = 2033

- Add the rounding up digit to the remainder to get the final remainder.

DO YOURSELF

A. Solve these sums **mentally** :

□ 7534 – 998

= (7534 – 1000) + 2 = 6534 + 2 = 6536

□ 8371 – 999

= (_____ – _____) + _____ = _____ + _____ = ☐

□ 6160 – 997

= (_____ – _____) + _____ = _____ + _____ = ☐

□ 8019 –996

= (_____ – _____) + _____ = _____ + _____ = ☐

□ 6851 – 993

= (_____ – _____) + _____ = _____ + _____ = ☐

□ 9724 – 995

= (_____ – _____) + _____ = _____ + _____ = ☐

□ 6381 – 994

= (_____ – _____) + _____ = _____ + _____ = ☐

□ 5243 – 998

= (_____ – _____) + _____ = _____ + _____ = ☐

B. Solve these problems **mentally** :

❐ A cart has 8193 watermelons loaded on it. 998 watermelons roll of the cart. How many watermelons are there on the cart now ?

= _____ – _____ = (_____ – _____) + ____ = _____ + _____ = [＿＿＿]

❐ There are 6852 students in a school. 995 of them are in the primary section. Find the number of students in the secondary section.

= _____ – _____ = (_____ – _____) + ____ = _____ + _____ = [＿＿＿]

❐ A herdsman owns 6618 cattle. He sells 994 cattle in a cattle fair. How many cattle are there in his herd now ?

= _____ – _____ = (_____ – _____) + ____ = _____ + _____ = [＿＿＿]

❐ A railway train had 9157 passengers in it at a station. 999 passengers got down there. How many passengers were left behind in the train ?

= _____ – _____ = (_____ – _____) + ____ = _____ + _____ = [＿＿＿]

❐ There were 7852 soldiers in a fort. 996 soldiers were sent to the battle-field. How many soldiers were left behind in the fort ?

= _____ – _____ = (_____ – _____) + ____ = _____ + _____ = [＿＿＿]

❐ A village had a population of 6688 people. 997 people left the village to settle in nearby towns. Find the new population of the village.

= _____ – _____ = (_____ – _____) + ____ = _____ + _____ = [＿＿＿]

❐ A city has a fleet of 7665 buses plying on its roads. 993 buses were dropped from the fleet for being defective. Find the number of the remaining buses.

= _____ – _____ = (_____ – _____) + ____ = _____ + _____ = [＿＿＿]

❐ A gardener had 6896 trees planted in rows. 992 old trees were felled to be replaced by new plants. Find the number of the remaining trees.

= _____ – _____ = (_____ – _____) + ____ = _____ + _____ = [＿＿＿]

❐ A flock had 9159 sheep. 998 sheep were sold off by the owner of the flock. How many sheep were left behind ?

= _____ – _____ = (_____ – _____) + ____ = _____ + _____ = [＿＿＿]

❐ A cloth mill had 7881 workers on its staff. 994 workers were dismissed from service. How many workers were left-behind ?

= _____ – _____ = (_____ – _____) + ____ = _____ + _____ = [＿＿＿]

READ CAREFULLY

- Round off the smaller numeral to the nearest **hundred** by adding a numeral.
- Subtract the hundreds from the higher numeral.
- Add the rounding numeral to the remainder to get the final remainder.

$$2573 - 586$$
$$= (2573 - 600) + 14$$
$$= 1973 + 14 = 1987$$

$$2573 - 586 = 1987$$

DO YOURSELF

A. Solve these sums mentally :

❏ $3815 - 186$
$= (3815 - 200) + 14 = 3615 + 14 = \boxed{3629}$

❏ $6852 - 883$
$= (_____ - \_\_\_\_\_) + \_\_\_\_ = _____ + \_\_\_\_ = \boxed{}$

❏ $7531 - 693$
$= (_____ - \_\_\_\_\_) + \_\_\_\_ = _____ + \_\_\_\_ = \boxed{}$

❏ $6187 - 375$
$= (_____ - \_\_\_\_\_) + \_\_\_\_ = _____ + \_\_\_\_ = \boxed{}$

❏ $4847 - 482$
$= (_____ - \_\_\_\_\_) + \_\_\_\_ = _____ + \_\_\_\_ = \boxed{}$

❏ $5862 - 689$
$= (_____ - \_\_\_\_\_) + \_\_\_\_ = _____ + \_\_\_\_ = \boxed{}$

❏ $9134 - 373$
$= (_____ - \_\_\_\_\_) + \_\_\_\_ = _____ + \_\_\_\_ = \boxed{}$

❏ $6735 - 687$
$= (_____ - \_\_\_\_\_) + \_\_\_\_ = _____ + \_\_\_\_ = \boxed{}$

B. Solve these problems **mentally** :

☐ A camel-cart had 3835 pumpkins loaded on it. 276 pumpkins rolled off the cart. How many pumpkins were left on the cart ?

= _____ – _____ = (_____ – _____) + _____ = _____ + _____ = ☐

☐ A school had 6781 students on its role. 387 students left the school on the eve of the new session. How many students were left behind in the school ?

= _____ – _____ = (_____ – _____) + _____ = _____ + _____ = ☐

☐ A factory had 6863 workers on its staff. 576 workers were sent to another branch of the factory. How many workers were left in the first factory ?

= _____ – _____ = (_____ – _____) + _____ = _____ + _____ = ☐

☐ A garden had 9073 trees in it. 589 old trees were felled to be replaced by new ones. How many trees were left behind ?

= _____ – _____ = (_____ – _____) + _____ = _____ + _____ = ☐

☐ A flock had 5868 sheep in it. Its owner sold off 592 sheep to another shepherd. How many sheep were left behind with him ?

= _____ – _____ = (_____ – _____) + _____ = _____ + _____ = ☐

☐ A metro-train had 6361 passengers at a station 478 passengers got down there. How many passengers were left behind in the train ?

= _____ – _____ = (_____ – _____) + _____ = _____ + _____ = ☐

☐ A village has a population of 8472 people. 484 people leave for a nearby town to look for jobs. How many people were left behind in the village ?

= _____ – _____ = (_____ – _____) + _____ = _____ + _____ = ☐

☐ A fort had 8486 soldiers in it. 589 soldiers were sent to the battle-front. How many soldiers were left behind in the forts ?

= _____ – _____ = (_____ – _____) + _____ = _____ + _____ = ☐

☐ A metro-city had 8742 buses plying on its roads. 884 buses were taken off the roads due to being road-unworthy. How many buses were left behind ?

= _____ – _____ = (_____ – _____) + _____ = _____ + _____ = ☐

☐ A cowherd had 7573 cows in his herd. He gave 681 cows in charity on the cow-worship day. How many cows were left behind with him ?

= _____ – _____ = (_____ – _____) + _____ = _____ + _____ = ☐

17 SUBTRACTING A STRING OF NUMERALS

- Arrange the numerals in pairs that can be easily grouped to the nearest tens.
- Then carry out the subtraction to get the final remainder.

$943 - 102 - 108 - 207 - 303$

$= 943 - (102 + 108) - (207 + 303)$

$= 943 - 210 - 510$

$= 943 - 720 = 223$

$943 - 102 - 108 - 207 - 303 = 223$

DO YOURSELF

A. Solve these sums mentally :

❑ $947 - 127 - 101 - 109 - 103$
$= 947 - (127 + 103) - (101 + 109) = 947 - 230 - 210 = 947 - 440 = \boxed{507}$

❑ $823 - 204 - 106 - 186 - 214$

= ___ − (___ + ___) − (___ + ___) = ___ − ___ − ___ = ___ − ___ = ☐

❑ $922 - 312 - 208 - 105 - 125$

= ___ − (___ + ___) − (___ + ___) = ___ − ___ − ___ = ___ − ___ = ☐

❑ $751 - 206 - 212 - 108 - 104$

= ___ − (___ + ___) − (___ + ___) = ___ − ___ − ___ = ___ − ___ = ☐

❑ $861 - 101 - 306 - 229 - 104$

= ___ − (___ + ___) − (___ + ___) = ___ − ___ − ___ = ___ − ___ = ☐

❑ $942 - 212 - 193 - 208 - 107$

= ___ − (___ + ___) − (___ + ___) = ___ − ___ − ___ = ___ − ___ = ☐

❑ $533 - 112 - 103 - 108 - 107$

= ___ − (___ + ___) − (___ + ___) = ___ − ___ − ___ = ___ − ___ = ☐

❑ $655 - 229 - 204 - 106 - 101$

= ___ − (___ + ___) − (___ + ___) = ___ − ___ − ___ = ___ − ___ = ☐

18 MULTIPLICATION BY 6—(I)

READ CAREFULLY

- $6 = 2 \times 3$

- Multiply at first by 2.

- Then multiply the product by 3 to get the final product.

$$9 \times 6$$
$$= 9 \times 3 \times 2$$
$$= 27 \times 2 = 54$$
$$\boxed{9 \times 6 = 54}$$

DO YOURSELF

A. Solve these sums **mentally** :

❐ 6×6 = $6 \times 2 \times 3 = 12 \times 3 = \boxed{36}$

❐ 4×6 = _____ × _____ × _____ = _____ × _____ = ☐

❐ 8×6 = _____ × _____ × _____ = _____ × _____ = ☐

❐ 5×6 = _____ × _____ × _____ = _____ × _____ = ☐

❐ 7×6 = _____ × _____ × _____ = _____ × _____ = ☐

❐ 1×6 = _____ × _____ × _____ = _____ × _____ = ☐

❐ 11×6 = _____ × _____ × _____ = _____ × _____ = ☐

❐ 12×6 = _____ × _____ × _____ = _____ × _____ = ☐

❐ 10×6 = _____ × _____ × _____ = _____ × _____ = ☐

❐ 3×6 = _____ × _____ × _____ = _____ × _____ = ☐

❐ 2×6 = _____ × _____ × _____ = _____ × _____ = ☐

(19) MULTIPLICATION BY 6—(II)

READ CAREFULLY

- $6 = 3 + 3$

- So multiply by 3 to get the product.

- Add this product to itself to get the **final product**.

5×6
$= 5 \times (3 + 3)$
$= 15 + 15 = 30$

$5 \times 6 = 30$

DO YOURSELF

A. Solve these sums mentally :

❑ $9 \times 6 \quad = 9 \times (3 + 3) = 27 + 27 = \boxed{54}$

❑ $2 \times 6 = \underline{\hspace{1cm}} \times (\underline{\hspace{0.5cm}} + \underline{\hspace{0.5cm}}) = \underline{\hspace{1cm}} + \underline{\hspace{1cm}} = $ ☐

❑ $3 \times 6 = \underline{\hspace{1cm}} \times (\underline{\hspace{0.5cm}} + \underline{\hspace{0.5cm}}) = \underline{\hspace{1cm}} + \underline{\hspace{1cm}} = $ ☐

❑ $4 \times 6 = \underline{\hspace{1cm}} \times (\underline{\hspace{0.5cm}} + \underline{\hspace{0.5cm}}) = \underline{\hspace{1cm}} + \underline{\hspace{1cm}} = $ ☐

❑ $1 \times 6 = \underline{\hspace{1cm}} \times (\underline{\hspace{0.5cm}} + \underline{\hspace{0.5cm}}) = \underline{\hspace{1cm}} + \underline{\hspace{1cm}} = $ ☐

❑ $6 \times 6 = \underline{\hspace{1cm}} \times (\underline{\hspace{0.5cm}} + \underline{\hspace{0.5cm}}) = \underline{\hspace{1cm}} + \underline{\hspace{1cm}} = $ ☐

❑ $7 \times 6 = \underline{\hspace{1cm}} \times (\underline{\hspace{0.5cm}} + \underline{\hspace{0.5cm}}) = \underline{\hspace{1cm}} + \underline{\hspace{1cm}} = $ ☐

❑ $8 \times 6 = \underline{\hspace{1cm}} \times (\underline{\hspace{0.5cm}} + \underline{\hspace{0.5cm}}) = \underline{\hspace{1cm}} + \underline{\hspace{1cm}} = $ ☐

❑ $5 \times 6 = \underline{\hspace{1cm}} \times (\underline{\hspace{0.5cm}} + \underline{\hspace{0.5cm}}) = \underline{\hspace{1cm}} + \underline{\hspace{1cm}} = $ ☐

❑ $10 \times 6 = \underline{\hspace{1cm}} \times (\underline{\hspace{0.5cm}} + \underline{\hspace{0.5cm}}) = \underline{\hspace{1cm}} + \underline{\hspace{1cm}} = $ ☐

❑ $11 \times 6 = \underline{\hspace{1cm}} \times (\underline{\hspace{0.5cm}} + \underline{\hspace{0.5cm}}) = \underline{\hspace{1cm}} + \underline{\hspace{1cm}} = $ ☐

❑ $12 \times 6 = \underline{\hspace{1cm}} \times (\underline{\hspace{0.5cm}} + \underline{\hspace{0.5cm}}) = \underline{\hspace{1cm}} + \underline{\hspace{1cm}} = $ ☐

READ CAREFULLY

- Break-up the other numeral into smaller parts.
- Multiply each part by 7 to get a product.
- Add up the products to get the **final product**.

5×7

$= (3 + 2) \times 7$

$= (3 \times 7) + (2 \times 7)$

$5 \times 7 = 35$

DO YOURSELF

A. Solve these sums **mentally** :

❏ $2 \times 7 = (1 + 1) \times 7 = (1 \times 7) + (1 \times 7) = 7 + 7 = \boxed{14}$

❏ $5 \times 7 = (\_\_ + \_\_) \times \_\_ = (\_\_ \times \_\_) + (\_\_ \times \_\_) = \_\_\_ + \_\_\_ = \boxed{}$

❏ $3 \times 7 = (\_\_ + \_\_) \times \_\_ = (\_\_ \times \_\_) + (\_\_ \times \_\_) = \_\_\_ + \_\_\_ = \boxed{}$

❏ $4 \times 7 = (\_\_ + \_\_) \times \_\_ = (\_\_ \times \_\_) + (\_\_ \times \_\_) = \_\_\_ + \_\_\_ = \boxed{}$

❏ $1 \times 7 = (\_\_ + \_\_) \times \_\_ = (\_\_ \times \_\_) + (\_\_ \times \_\_) = \_\_\_ + \_\_\_ = \boxed{}$

❏ $6 \times 7 = (\_\_ + \_\_) \times \_\_ = (\_\_ \times \_\_) + (\_\_ \times \_\_) = \_\_\_ + \_\_\_ = \boxed{}$

❏ $7 \times 7 = (\_\_ + \_\_) \times \_\_ = (\_\_ \times \_\_) + (\_\_ \times \_\_) = \_\_\_ + \_\_\_ = \boxed{}$

❏ $8 \times 7 = (\_\_ + \_\_) \times \_\_ = (\_\_ \times \_\_) + (\_\_ \times \_\_) = \_\_\_ + \_\_\_ = \boxed{}$

❏ $9 \times 7 = (\_\_ + \_\_) \times \_\_ = (\_\_ \times \_\_) + (\_\_ \times \_\_) = \_\_\_ + \_\_\_ = \boxed{}$

❏ $10 \times 7 = (\_\_ + \_\_) \times \_\_ = (\_\_ \times \_\_) + (\_\_ \times \_\_) = \_\_\_ + \_\_\_ = \boxed{}$

❏ $11 \times 7 = (\_\_ + \_\_) \times \_\_ = (\_\_ \times \_\_) + (\_\_ \times \_\_) = \_\_\_ + \_\_\_ = \boxed{}$

❏ $12 \times 7 = (\_\_ + \_\_) \times \_\_ = (\_\_ \times \_\_) + (\_\_ \times \_\_) = \_\_\_ + \_\_\_ = \boxed{}$

READ CAREFULLY

- 7 = 10 – 3
- Multiply the other numeral by 10 to get a product.
- Then multiply it by 3 to get another product.
- Subtract the second product from the first product to get the **final product**.

$$5 \times 7$$
$$= 5 \times (10 - 3)$$
$$= (5 \times 10) - (5 \times 3)$$
$$= 50 - 15 = 35$$

$$5 \times 7 = 35$$

DO YOURSELF

A. Do these sums mentally :

❒ $1 \times 7 = 1 \times (10 - 3) = (1 \times 10) - (1 \times 3) = 10 - 3 = \boxed{7}$

❒ $2 \times 7 = \_\_ \times (\_\_ - \_\_) = (\_\_ \times \_\_) - (\_\_ \times \_\_) = \_\_ - \_\_ = \boxed{}$

❒ $3 \times 7 = \_\_ \times (\_\_ - \_\_) = (\_\_ \times \_\_) - (\_\_ \times \_\_) = \_\_ - \_\_ = \boxed{}$

❒ $4 \times 7 = \_\_ \times (\_\_ - \_\_) = (\_\_ \times \_\_) - (\_\_ \times \_\_) = \_\_ - \_\_ = \boxed{}$

❒ $5 \times 7 = \_\_ \times (\_\_ - \_\_) = (\_\_ \times \_\_) - (\_\_ \times \_\_) = \_\_ - \_\_ = \boxed{}$

❒ $6 \times 7 = \_\_ \times (\_\_ - \_\_) = (\_\_ \times \_\_) - (\_\_ \times \_\_) = \_\_ - \_\_ = \boxed{}$

❒ $7 \times 7 = \_\_ \times (\_\_ - \_\_) = (\_\_ \times \_\_) - (\_\_ \times \_\_) = \_\_ - \_\_ = \boxed{}$

❒ $8 \times 7 = \_\_ \times (\_\_ - \_\_) = (\_\_ \times \_\_) - (\_\_ \times \_\_) = \_\_ - \_\_ = \boxed{}$

❒ $9 \times 7 = \_\_ \times (\_\_ - \_\_) = (\_\_ \times \_\_) - (\_\_ \times \_\_) = \_\_ - \_\_ = \boxed{}$

❒ $10 \times 7 = \_\_ \times (\_\_ - \_\_) = (\_\_ \times \_\_) - (\_\_ \times \_\_) = \_\_ - \_\_ = \boxed{}$

❒ $11 \times 7 = \_\_ \times (\_\_ - \_\_) = (\_\_ \times \_\_) - (\_\_ \times \_\_) = \_\_ - \_\_ = \boxed{}$

❒ $12 \times 7 = \_\_ \times (\_\_ - \_\_) = (\_\_ \times \_\_) - (\_\_ \times \_\_) = \_\_ - \_\_ = \boxed{}$

22 MULTIPLICATION BY 8—(I)

READ CAREFULLY

- $8 = 2 \times 4$

- So multiply the other numeral by 2 to get a product.

- Multiply this product by 4 to get the final product.

$$5 \times 8$$
$$= 5 \times 2 \times 4$$
$$= 10 \times 4 = 40$$
$$5 \times 8 = 40$$

DO YOURSELF

A. Do these sums **mentally** :

❑ 1×8 $= 1 \times 2 \times 4 = 2 \times 4 =$ **8**

❑ 2×8 = _____ × _____ × _____ = _____ × _____ = ☐

❑ 3×8 = _____ × _____ × _____ = _____ × _____ = ☐

❑ 4×8 = _____ × _____ × _____ = _____ × _____ = ☐

❑ 5×8 = _____ × _____ × _____ = _____ × _____ = ☐

❑ 6×8 = _____ × _____ × _____ = _____ × _____ = ☐

❑ 7×8 = _____ × _____ × _____ = _____ × _____ = ☐

❑ 8×8 = _____ × _____ × _____ = _____ × _____ = ☐

❑ 9×8 = _____ × _____ × _____ = _____ × _____ = ☐

❑ 10×8 = _____ × _____ × _____ = _____ × _____ = ☐

❑ 11×8 = _____ × _____ × _____ = _____ × _____ = ☐

❑ 12×8 = _____ × _____ × _____ = _____ × _____ = ☐

(23) MULTIPLICATION BY 8—(II)

READ CAREFULLY

- $8 = 4 + 4$
- Multiply the other numeral by 4 to get a product.
- Then add this product to itself to get the **final product**.

$$5 \times 8$$
$$= 5 \times (4 + 4)$$
$$= (5 \times 4) + (5 \times 4)$$
$$= 20 + 20 = 40$$
$$5 \times 8 = 40$$

DO YOURSELF

A. Do these sums mentally :

❑ $1 \times 8 \quad = 1 \times (4 + 4) = 4 + 4 = \boxed{8}$

❑ $2 \times 8 \quad = \underline{\quad} \times (\underline{\quad} + \underline{\quad}) = \underline{\quad} + \underline{\quad} = \boxed{}$

❑ $3 \times 8 \quad = \underline{\quad} \times (\underline{\quad} + \underline{\quad}) = \underline{\quad} + \underline{\quad} = \boxed{}$

❑ $4 \times 8 \quad = \underline{\quad} \times (\underline{\quad} + \underline{\quad}) = \underline{\quad} + \underline{\quad} = \boxed{}$

❑ $5 \times 8 \quad = \underline{\quad} \times (\underline{\quad} + \underline{\quad}) = \underline{\quad} + \underline{\quad} = \boxed{}$

❑ $6 \times 8 \quad = \underline{\quad} \times (\underline{\quad} + \underline{\quad}) = \underline{\quad} + \underline{\quad} = \boxed{}$

❑ $7 \times 8 \quad = \underline{\quad} \times (\underline{\quad} + \underline{\quad}) = \underline{\quad} + \underline{\quad} = \boxed{}$

❑ $8 \times 8 \quad = \underline{\quad} \times (\underline{\quad} + \underline{\quad}) = \underline{\quad} + \underline{\quad} = \boxed{}$

❑ $9 \times 8 \quad = \underline{\quad} \times (\underline{\quad} + \underline{\quad}) = \underline{\quad} + \underline{\quad} = \boxed{}$

❑ $10 \times 8 = \underline{\quad} \times (\underline{\quad} + \underline{\quad}) = \underline{\quad} + \underline{\quad} = \boxed{}$

❑ $11 \times 8 = \underline{\quad} \times (\underline{\quad} + \underline{\quad}) = \underline{\quad} + \underline{\quad} = \boxed{}$

❑ $12 \times 8 = \underline{\quad} \times (\underline{\quad} + \underline{\quad}) = \underline{\quad} + \underline{\quad} = \boxed{}$

(24) MULTIPLICATION BY 8—(III)

- 8 = 10 − 2
- Multiply the numeral by 10 to get a product.
- Multiply the numeral by 2 also to get another product.
- Subtract the second product from the first product to get the **final product**.

5×8
$= 5 \times (10 - 2)$
$= (5 \times 10) - (5 \times 2)$
$= 50 - 10 = 40$
$5 \times 8 = 40$

DO YOURSELF

A. Do these sums mentally :

☐ $1 \times 8 = 1 \times (10 - 2) = (1 \times 10) - (1 \times 2) = 10 - 2 = \boxed{8}$

☐ $2 \times 8 = \_\_ \times (\_\_ - \_\_) = (\_\_ \times \_\_) - (\_\_ \times \_\_) = \_\_ - \_\_ = \boxed{}$

☐ $3 \times 8 = \_\_ \times (\_\_ - \_\_) = (\_\_ \times \_\_) - (\_\_ \times \_\_) = \_\_ - \_\_ = \boxed{}$

☐ $4 \times 8 = \_\_ \times (\_\_ - \_\_) = (\_\_ \times \_\_) - (\_\_ \times \_\_) = \_\_ - \_\_ = \boxed{}$

☐ $5 \times 8 = \_\_ \times (\_\_ - \_\_) = (\_\_ \times \_\_) - (\_\_ \times \_\_) = \_\_ - \_\_ = \boxed{}$

☐ $6 \times 8 = \_\_ \times (\_\_ - \_\_) = (\_\_ \times \_\_) - (\_\_ \times \_\_) = \_\_ - \_\_ = \boxed{}$

☐ $7 \times 8 = \_\_ \times (\_\_ - \_\_) = (\_\_ \times \_\_) - (\_\_ \times \_\_) = \_\_ - \_\_ = \boxed{}$

☐ $8 \times 8 = \_\_ \times (\_\_ - \_\_) = (\_\_ \times \_\_) - (\_\_ \times \_\_) = \_\_ - \_\_ = \boxed{}$

☐ $9 \times 8 = \_\_ \times (\_\_ - \_\_) = (\_\_ \times \_\_) - (\_\_ \times \_\_) = \_\_ - \_\_ = \boxed{}$

☐ $10 \times 8 = \_\_ \times (\_\_ - \_\_) = (\_\_ \times \_\_) - (\_\_ \times \_\_) = \_\_ - \_\_ = \boxed{}$

☐ $11 \times 8 = \_\_ \times (\_\_ - \_\_) = (\_\_ \times \_\_) - (\_\_ \times \_\_) = \_\_ - \_\_ = \boxed{}$

☐ $12 \times 8 = \_\_ \times (\_\_ - \_\_) = (\_\_ \times \_\_) - (\_\_ \times \_\_) = \_\_ - \_\_ = \boxed{}$

25 MULTIPLICATION BY 9—(I)

READ CAREFULLY

- $9 = 3 \times 3$

- Multiply the other numeral by 3 to get a product.

- Multiply this product again by 3 to get the final product.

5×9

$= 5 \times 3 \times 3$

$= 15 \times 3 = 45$

$5 \times 9 = 45$

DO YOURSELF

A. Solve these sums **mentally** :

❏ $1 \times 9 = 1 \times 3 \times 3 = 3 \times 3 = \boxed{9}$

❏ $2 \times 9 = \underline{\quad} \times \underline{\quad} \times \underline{\quad} = \underline{\qquad} \times \underline{\qquad} =$

❏ $3 \times 9 = \underline{\quad} \times \underline{\quad} \times \underline{\quad} = \underline{\qquad} \times \underline{\qquad} =$

❏ $4 \times 9 = \underline{\quad} \times \underline{\quad} \times \underline{\quad} = \underline{\qquad} \times \underline{\qquad} =$

❏ $5 \times 9 = \underline{\quad} \times \underline{\quad} \times \underline{\quad} = \underline{\qquad} \times \underline{\qquad} =$

❏ $6 \times 9 = \underline{\quad} \times \underline{\quad} \times \underline{\quad} = \underline{\qquad} \times \underline{\qquad} =$

❏ $7 \times 9 = \underline{\quad} \times \underline{\quad} \times \underline{\quad} = \underline{\qquad} \times \underline{\qquad} =$

❏ $8 \times 9 = \underline{\quad} \times \underline{\quad} \times \underline{\quad} = \underline{\qquad} \times \underline{\qquad} =$

❏ $10 \times 9 = \underline{\quad} \times \underline{\quad} \times \underline{\quad} = \underline{\qquad} \times \underline{\qquad} =$

❏ $11 \times 9 = \underline{\quad} \times \underline{\quad} \times \underline{\quad} = \underline{\qquad} \times \underline{\qquad} =$

❏ $12 \times 9 = \underline{\quad} \times \underline{\quad} \times \underline{\quad} = \underline{\qquad} \times \underline{\qquad} =$

26 MULTIPLICATION BY 9—(II)

READ CAREFULLY

- $9 = 10 - 1$

- Multiply the other numeral by **10** to get a product.

- Subtract the other numeral from this product to get the **final product**.

5×9
$= 5 \times (10 - 1)$
$= 50 - 5 = 45$

$5 \times 9 = 45$

DO YOURSELF

A. Solve these sums mentally :

❐ $1 \times 9 \quad = 1 \times (10 - 1) = 10 - 1 = \boxed{9}$

❐ $2 \times 9 \quad = \underline{} \times (\underline{} - \underline{}) = \underline{} - \underline{} =$

❐ $3 \times 9 \quad = \underline{} \times (\underline{} - \underline{}) = \underline{} - \underline{} =$

❐ $4 \times 9 \quad = \underline{} \times (\underline{} - \underline{}) = \underline{} - \underline{} =$

❐ $5 \times 9 \quad = \underline{} \times (\underline{} - \underline{}) = \underline{} - \underline{} =$

❐ $6 \times 9 \quad = \underline{} \times (\underline{} - \underline{}) = \underline{} - \underline{} =$

❐ $7 \times 9 \quad = \underline{} \times (\underline{} - \underline{}) = \underline{} - \underline{} =$

❐ $8 \times 9 \quad = \underline{} \times (\underline{} - \underline{}) = \underline{} - \underline{} =$

❐ $9 \times 9 \quad = \underline{} \times (\underline{} - \underline{}) = \underline{} - \underline{} =$

❐ $10 \times 9 \quad = \underline{} \times (\underline{} - \underline{}) = \underline{} - \underline{} =$

❐ $11 \times 9 \quad = \underline{} \times (\underline{} - \underline{}) = \underline{} - \underline{} =$

(27) MULTIPLICATION BY 11

- 11 = 10 + 1

- Multiply the other numeral by **10** to get a product.

- **Add** the other numeral to this product to get the final product.

$$5 \times 11$$
$$= 5 \times (10 + 1)$$
$$= 50 + 5 = 55$$

$$5 \times 11 = 55$$

DO YOURSELF

A. Solve these sums mentally :

- ❏ $1 \times 11 = 1 \times (10 + 1) = 10 + 1 = \boxed{11}$

- ❏ $2 \times 11 = \underline{} \times (\underline{} + \underline{}) = \underline{} + \underline{} = \boxed{}$

- ❏ $3 \times 11 = \underline{} \times (\underline{} + \underline{}) = \underline{} + \underline{} = \boxed{}$

- ❏ $4 \times 11 = \underline{} \times (\underline{} + \underline{}) = \underline{} + \underline{} = \boxed{}$

- ❏ $5 \times 11 = \underline{} \times (\underline{} + \underline{}) = \underline{} + \underline{} = \boxed{}$

- ❏ $6 \times 11 = \underline{} \times (\underline{} + \underline{}) = \underline{} + \underline{} = \boxed{}$

- ❏ $7 \times 11 = \underline{} \times (\underline{} + \underline{}) = \underline{} + \underline{} = \boxed{}$

- ❏ $8 \times 11 = \underline{} \times (\underline{} + \underline{}) = \underline{} + \underline{} = \boxed{}$

- ❏ $9 \times 11 = \underline{} \times (\underline{} + \underline{}) = \underline{} + \underline{} = \boxed{}$

- ❏ $10 \times 11 = \underline{} \times (\underline{} + \underline{}) = \underline{} + \underline{} = \boxed{}$

- ❏ $11 \times 11 = \underline{} \times (\underline{} + \underline{}) = \underline{} + \underline{} = \boxed{}$

READ CAREFULLY

- Break-up the numeral to be multiplied into **hundreds**, **tens** and **ones**.

- Multiply them by the numeral in turn.

- Add up all the products to get the **final product**.

462×7
$= (400 \times 7) + (60 \times 7) + (2 \times 7)$
$= 2800 + 420 + 14$
$= 3234$

$462 \times 7 = 3234$

DO YOURSELF

A. **Solve these sums by break-up method mentally :**

❐ 128×9

$= (100 \times 9) + (20 \times 9) + (8 \times 9) = 900 + 180 + 72 = \boxed{1152}$

❐ 690×4

$= (\_\_\times\_\_) + (\_\_\_ \times \_\_) + (\_\_\_\times \_\_) = \_\_ + \_\_ + \_\_ = \boxed{}$

❐ 584×7

$= (\_\_\times\_\_) + (\_\_\_ \times \_\_) + (\_\_\_\times \_\_) = \_\_ + \_\_ + \_\_ = \boxed{}$

❐ 862×5

$= (\_\_\times\_\_) + (\_\_\_ \times \_\_) + (\_\_\_\times \_\_) = \_\_ + \_\_ + \_\_ = \boxed{}$

❐ 733×8

$= (\_\_\times\_\_) + (\_\_\_ \times \_\_) + (\_\_\_\times \_\_) = \_\_ + \_\_ + \_\_ = \boxed{}$

❐ 906×2

$= (\_\_\times\_\_) + (\_\_\_ \times \_\_) + (\_\_\_\times \_\_) = \_\_ + \_\_ + \_\_ = \boxed{}$

❐ 732×6

$= (\_\_\times\_\_) + (\_\_\_ \times \_\_) + (\_\_\_\times \_\_) = \_\_ + \_\_ + \_\_ = \boxed{}$

READ CAREFULLY

- Break-up the numeral to be multiplied into thousands, hundreds, tens and ones.
- Multiply them by the other numeral in turn and add up to get the final product.

1639×3

$= (1000 \times 3) + (600 \times 3) + (30 \times 3) + (9 \times 3)$

$= 3000 + 1800 + 90 + 27$

$= 4000 + 900 + 17 = 4917$

$1639 \times 3 = 4917$

DO YOURSELF

A. Solve these sums **mentally by break-up method** :

❏ 1573×4

$= (1000 \times 4) + (500 \times 4) + (70 \times 4) + (3 \times 4))$
$= 4000 + 2000 + 280 + 12 = 6000 + 280 + 12 = \boxed{6292}$

❏ 1822×3

$= (\underline{\hspace{1cm}} \times \underline{\hspace{1cm}}) + (\underline{\hspace{1cm}} \times \underline{\hspace{1cm}}) + (\underline{\hspace{1cm}} \times \underline{\hspace{1cm}}) + (\underline{\hspace{0.5cm}} \times \underline{\hspace{0.5cm}})$

$= \underline{\hspace{1cm}} + \underline{\hspace{1cm}} + \underline{\hspace{1cm}} + \underline{\hspace{1cm}} = \underline{\hspace{1cm}} + \underline{\hspace{1cm}} + \underline{\hspace{1cm}} = \boxed{}$

❏ 1826×5

$= (\underline{\hspace{1cm}} \times \underline{\hspace{1cm}}) + (\underline{\hspace{1cm}} \times \underline{\hspace{1cm}}) + (\underline{\hspace{1cm}} \times \underline{\hspace{1cm}}) + (\underline{\hspace{0.5cm}} \times \underline{\hspace{0.5cm}})$

$= \underline{\hspace{1cm}} + \underline{\hspace{1cm}} + \underline{\hspace{1cm}} + \underline{\hspace{1cm}} = \underline{\hspace{1cm}} + \underline{\hspace{1cm}} + \underline{\hspace{1cm}} = \boxed{}$

❏ 3735×2

$= (\underline{\hspace{1cm}} \times \underline{\hspace{1cm}}) + (\underline{\hspace{1cm}} \times \underline{\hspace{1cm}}) + (\underline{\hspace{1cm}} \times \underline{\hspace{1cm}}) + (\underline{\hspace{0.5cm}} \times \underline{\hspace{0.5cm}})$

$= \underline{\hspace{1cm}} + \underline{\hspace{1cm}} + \underline{\hspace{1cm}} + \underline{\hspace{1cm}} = \underline{\hspace{1cm}} + \underline{\hspace{1cm}} + \underline{\hspace{1cm}} = \boxed{}$

❏ 1247×7

$= (\underline{\hspace{1cm}} \times \underline{\hspace{1cm}}) + (\underline{\hspace{1cm}} \times \underline{\hspace{1cm}}) + (\underline{\hspace{1cm}} \times \underline{\hspace{1cm}}) + (\underline{\hspace{0.5cm}} \times \underline{\hspace{0.5cm}})$

$= \underline{\hspace{1cm}} + \underline{\hspace{1cm}} + \underline{\hspace{1cm}} + \underline{\hspace{1cm}} = \underline{\hspace{1cm}} + \underline{\hspace{1cm}} + \underline{\hspace{1cm}} = \boxed{}$

30 MULTIPLICATION : PROBLEMS

READ CAREFULLY

- Read the problem carefully.
- Carry out the multiplication using the break-up method.
- Observe the problem and its solution given in front.

A library has 8 almirahs and each almirah has 288 books. How many books are there in all ?

Almirahs = 8   No. of books = 288
Total books = 288 × 8 = (200 × 8) + (80 × 8) + (8 × 8)
= 1600 + 640 + 64
= 1600 + 600 + 40 + 60 + 4
= 2200 + 100 + 4 = 2304

DO YOURSELF

A. Solve these problems mentally :

❏ A basket has 268 apples. How many apples will there be in 7 such baskets ?

268 × 7

= (____ × ___) + (____ × ___) + (___ × ___) = ____ + ____ + ___ = ☐

❏ A sack of rice costs Rs 285. Find the cost of 9 such sacks.

285 × 9

= (____ × ___) + (____ × ___) + (___ × ___) = ____ + ____ + ___ = ☐

❏ A carton has 450 shawls. How many shawls will there be in 6 such cartons ?

450 × 6

= (____ × ___) + (____ × ___) + (___ × ___) = ____ + ____ + ___ = ☐

❏ A library has 5 almirahs each with 278 books. Find the total number of books.

278 × 5

= (____ × ___) + (____ × ___) + (___ × ___) = ____ + ____ + ___ = ☐

❏ A book consists of 384 pages. How many pages will there be in 9 such books ?

384 × 9

= (____ × ___) + (____ × ___) + (___ × ___) = ____ + ____ + ___ = ☐

❏ A factory makes 875 lamps daily. How many lamps will it make in seven days ?

875 × 7

= (____ × ___) + (____ × ___) + (___ × ___) = ____ + ____ + ___ = ☐

31 DIVISION BY 2

- Observe the numeral to be divided for its digit in the **one's place**.

- If this digit can be divided by 2, the entire numeral can be divided by 2.

- The division can be done by break-up method.

Can 238 be divided by 2 ?

The one's digit in the numeral is 8 which can be divided by 2.

So 238 can be divided by 2.

$238 \div 2$

$= (200 \div 2) + (30 \div 2) + (8 \div 2)$

$= 100 + 15 + 4 = 119$

DO YOURSELF

A. Write **Yes** if the numeral can be divided by 2. If not, write **No** :

❐ Can 237 be divided by 2 ? _____

❐ Can 426 be divided by 2 ? _____

❐ Can 733 be divided by 2 ? _____

❐ Can 642 be divided by 2 ? _____

❐ Can 847 be divided by 2 ? _____

❐ Can 512 be divided by 2 ? _____

B. Divide by **break-up** method :

❐ $856 \div 2$

$= (800 \div 2) + (50 \div 2) + (6 \div 2) = 400 + 25 + 3 = \boxed{428}$

❐ $642 \div 2 = ($ _____ $\div$ _____ $) + ($ _____ $\div$ _____ $) + ($ _____ $\div$ _____ $)$

$= $ _____ $+$ _____ $+$ _____ $=$

❐ $784 \div 2 = ($ _____ $\div$ _____ $) + ($ _____ $\div$ _____ $) + ($ _____ $\div$ _____ $)$

$= $ _____ $+$ _____ $+$ _____ $=$

❐ $824 \div 2 = ($ _____ $\div$ _____ $) + ($ _____ $\div$ _____ $) + ($ _____ $\div$ _____ $)$

$= $ _____ $+$ _____ $+$ _____ $=$

C. Solve these problems mentally :

❒ A basket has 624 oranges. 2 oranges are to be given to one beggar. How many beggar must be there for all the oranges ?

_____ ÷ ___ = (_____ ÷ _____) + (_____ ÷ _____) + (_____ ÷ _____)

= _____ + _____ + _____ = [   ]

❒ There are 416 people in a club. How many couples will they make ?

_____ ÷ ___ = (_____ ÷ _____) + (_____ ÷ _____) + (_____ ÷ _____)

= _____ + _____ + _____ = [   ]

❒ There were 654 cattle in a fair. If a farmer buys 2 cattle, how many farmers will buy all the cattle ?

_____ ÷ ___ = (_____ ÷ _____) + (_____ ÷ _____) + (_____ ÷ _____)

= _____ + _____ + _____ = [   ]

❒ 726 marbles are to be divided among children. If each child gets 2 marbles, how many children will take away all the marbles ?

_____ ÷ ___ = (_____ ÷ _____) + (_____ ÷ _____) + (_____ ÷ _____)

= _____ + _____ + _____ = [   ]

❒ 964 passengers board a train. 2 passenger can sit on a seat. How many seats are needed for all the passengers ?

_____ ÷ ___ = (_____ ÷ _____) + (_____ ÷ _____) + (_____ ÷ _____)

= _____ + _____ + _____ = [   ]

❒ A school has 426 students in all. 2 students can sit at a desk. How many desks are needed for all the students ?

_____ ÷ ___ = (_____ ÷ _____) + (_____ ÷ _____) + (_____ ÷ _____)

= _____ + _____ + _____ = [   ]

❒ A cart has 354 melons loaded on it. 2 melons are sold for a dollar. How many dollars are needed to buy all the melons ?

_____ ÷ ___ = (_____ ÷ _____) + (_____ ÷ _____) + (_____ ÷ _____)

= _____ + _____ + _____ = [   ]

❒ If 2 toffees are given to a child, how many children will take 424 toffees ?

_____ ÷ ___ = (_____ ÷ _____) + (_____ ÷ _____) + (_____ ÷ _____)

= _____ + _____ + _____ = [   ]

32 DIVISION BY 3

READ CAREFULLY

- Add up the digits of the given numeral to find their **sum**.

- If this sum can be divided by 3, the numeral can also be divided by 3.

- The division can be done by break-up method.

Can 363 be divided by 3 ?

The sum of the digits 3, 6, 3 is 12 which can be divided by 3.

So 363 can be divided by 3.

$363 \div 3$

$= (300 \div 3) + (60 \div 3) + (3 \div 3)$

$= 100 + 20 + 1 = 121$

DO YOURSELF

A. Write Yes if the numeral can be divided by 3. If not, write No :

- ☐ Can 147 be divided by 3 ? _____

- ☐ Can 819 be divided by 3 ? _____

- ☐ Can 625 be divided by 3 ? _____

- ☐ Can 764 be divided by 3 ? _____

- ☐ Can 726 be divided by 3 ? _____

- ☐ Can 488 be divided by 3 ? _____

B. Divide by break-up method :

- ☐ $636 \div 3$

  $= (600 \div 3) + (30 \div 3) + (6 \div 3) = 200 + 10 + 2 = \boxed{212}$

- ☐ $363 \div 3 = (\rule{1cm}{0.4pt} \div \rule{1cm}{0.4pt}) + (\rule{1cm}{0.4pt} \div \rule{1cm}{0.4pt}) + (\rule{1cm}{0.4pt} \div \rule{1cm}{0.4pt})$

  $= \rule{1cm}{0.4pt} + \rule{1cm}{0.4pt} + \rule{1cm}{0.4pt} =$

- ☐ $993 \div 3 = (\rule{1cm}{0.4pt} \div \rule{1cm}{0.4pt}) + (\rule{1cm}{0.4pt} \div \rule{1cm}{0.4pt}) + (\rule{1cm}{0.4pt} \div \rule{1cm}{0.4pt})$

  $= \rule{1cm}{0.4pt} + \rule{1cm}{0.4pt} + \rule{1cm}{0.4pt} =$

- ☐ $696 \div 3 = (\rule{1cm}{0.4pt} \div \rule{1cm}{0.4pt}) + (\rule{1cm}{0.4pt} \div \rule{1cm}{0.4pt}) + (\rule{1cm}{0.4pt} \div \rule{1cm}{0.4pt})$

  $= \rule{1cm}{0.4pt} + \rule{1cm}{0.4pt} + \rule{1cm}{0.4pt} =$

C. Solve these problems **mentally** :

❑ A box has 936 toffees. 3 toffees are to be given to a child. How many children must be there for all the toffees ?

_____ ÷ ___ = (_____ ÷ _____) + (_____ ÷ _____) + (_____ ÷ _____)

= _____ + _____ + _____ = [   ]

❑ A heap has 3366 marbles. How many sets of 3's can they be made into ?

_____ ÷ ___ = (_____ ÷ _____) + (_____ ÷ _____) + (_____ ÷ _____)

= _____ + _____ + _____ = [   ]

❑ There are 333 watermelons on a cart. If 3 melons cost a dollar, how many dollars can buy all the watermelons ?

_____ ÷ ___ = (_____ ÷ _____) + (_____ ÷ _____) + (_____ ÷ _____)

= _____ ÷ _____ + _____ = [   ]

❑ 969 biscuits are to be given to beggars. If each beggar gets 3 biscuits, find the number of beggars.

_____ ÷ ___ = (_____ ÷ _____) + (_____ ÷ _____) + (_____ ÷ _____)

= _____ ÷ _____ + _____ = [   ]

❑ 963 passengers board a train. If 3 passengers occupy a berth, how many berths are needed for all the passengers ?

_____ ÷ ___ = (_____ ÷ _____) + (_____ ÷ _____) + (_____ ÷ _____)

= _____ ÷ _____ + _____ = [   ]

❑ A school has 6699 students in all. 3 students can sit at a desk. How many desks are needed for all the students ?

_____ ÷ ___ = (_____ ÷ _____) + (_____ ÷ _____) + (_____ ÷ _____)

= _____ + _____ + _____ = [   ]

❑ There are 3669 people in a village. If each family has 3 members, find the number of families in the village.

_____ ÷ ___ = (_____ ÷ _____) + (_____ ÷ _____) + (_____ ÷ _____)

= _____ + _____ + _____ = [   ]

❑ If 3 candies are given to a child, how many children will take 639 candies ?

_____ ÷ ___ = (_____ ÷ _____) + (_____ ÷ _____) + (_____ ÷ _____)

= _____ + _____ + _____ = [   ]

33 DIVISION BY 4

READ CAREFULLY

- Observe the two right-hand digits of the numeral to be divided.
- If these digits make a numeral divisible by 4, the given numeral can also be divided by 4.
- The division can be done by break-up method.

Can 844 be divided by 4 ?

The two right-hand digits make the numeral 44 which is divisible by 4.

So 844 is also divisible by 4.

$$844 \div 4$$
$$= (800 \div 4) + (40 \div 4) + (4 \div 4)$$
$$= 200 + 10 + 1 = 211$$

DO YOURSELF

A. Write **Yes** if the numeral can be divided by 4. If not, write **No** :

- Can 506 be divided by 4 ?   _____
- Can 828 be divided by 4 ?   _____
- Can 2284 be divided by 4 ?   _____
- Can 135 be divided by 4 ?   _____
- Can 925 be divided by 4 ?   _____
- Can 848 be divided by 4 ?   _____

B. Divide by **break-up** method :

- $484 \div 4$
  $$= (400 \div 4) + (80 \div 4) + (4 \div 4) = 100 + 20 + 2 = \boxed{122}$$

- $824 \div 4 = (\underline{\quad} \div \underline{\quad}) + (\underline{\quad} \div \underline{\quad}) + (\underline{\quad} \div \underline{\quad})$
  $$= \underline{\quad} + \underline{\quad} + \underline{\quad} =$$

- $840 \div 4 = (\underline{\quad} \div \underline{\quad}) + (\underline{\quad} \div \underline{\quad}) + (\underline{\quad} \div \underline{\quad})$
  $$= \underline{\quad} + \underline{\quad} + \underline{\quad} =$$

- $8464 \div 4 = (\underline{\quad} \div \underline{\quad}) + (\underline{\quad} \div \underline{\quad}) + (\underline{\quad} \div \underline{\quad})$
  $$= \underline{\quad} + \underline{\quad} + \underline{\quad} =$$

C. Solve these problems **mentally** :

❏ A village has a population of 4880 people. How many families are there in it, if each family has 4 members ?

_____ ÷ ___ = (_____ ÷ _____) + (_____ ÷ _____) + (_____ ÷ _____)

= _____ + _____ + _____ =

❏ Into how many sets of 4 each can 888 marbles be made into ?

_____ ÷ ___ = (_____ ÷ _____) + (_____ ÷ _____) + (_____ ÷ _____)

= _____ + _____ + _____ =

❏ 424 people are to cross a river. If a boat can carry 4 people, how many boats are needed to take all the people across the river ?

_____ ÷ ___ = (_____ ÷ _____) + (_____ ÷ _____) + (_____ ÷ _____)

= _____ + _____ + _____ =

❏ 8428 cookies are to be divided among beggars. If each beggar gets 4 cookies, how many beggars will take away all the cookies ?

_____ ÷ ___ = (_____ ÷ _____) + (_____ ÷ _____) + (_____ ÷ _____)

= _____ + _____ + _____ =

❏ 6848 passengers board a train. If each berth is for 4 passengers, how many berths are needed for all the passengers ?

_____ ÷ ___ = (_____ ÷ _____) + (_____ ÷ _____) + (_____ ÷ _____)

= _____ + _____ + _____ =

❏ 4484 rose flowers are to be picked from rose bushes. If each bush has 4 flowers, how many bushes will provide the needed flowers ?

_____ ÷ ___ = (_____ ÷ _____) + (_____ ÷ _____) + (_____ ÷ _____)

= _____ + _____ + _____ =

❏ 488 eggs are to be placed on plates. If each plate has 4 eggs, how many plates are needed for all the eggs ?

_____ ÷ ___ = (_____ ÷ _____) + (_____ ÷ _____) + (_____ ÷ _____)

= _____ + _____ + _____ =

❏ How many tables with 4 seats each are needed for 884 guests ?

_____ ÷ ___ = (_____ ÷ _____) + (_____ ÷ _____) + (_____ ÷ _____)

= _____ + _____ + _____ =

(34) DIVISION BY 5

READ CAREFULLY

- Observe the digit in the **one's place** of the given numeral.

- If it is 0 or 5, the numeral is divisible by 5.

- The division can be done by break-up method.

Can 135 be divided by 5 ?
The digit in the one's place is 5.
So 135 is divisible by 5.

$135 \div 5$

$= (100 \div 5) + (30 \div 5) + (5 \div 5)$

$= 20 + 6 + 1 = 27$

$135 \div 5 = 27$

DO YOURSELF

A. Write Yes if the number can be divided by 5. If not, write No :

- Can 315 be divided by 5 ? _____
- Can 728 be divided by 5 ? _____
- Can 460 be divided by 5 ? _____
- Can 293 be divided by 5 ? _____
- Can 895 be divided by 5 ? _____
- Can 616 be divided by 5 ? _____

B. Divide by break-up method :

- $525 \div 5$

    $= (500 \div 5) + (20 \div 5) + (5 \div 5) = 100 + 4 + 1 = \boxed{105}$

- $420 \div 5 = (\underline{} \div \underline{}) + (\underline{} \div \underline{}) + (\underline{} \div \underline{})$

    $= \underline{} + \underline{} + \underline{} = $

- $390 \div 5 = (\underline{} \div \underline{}) + (\underline{} \div \underline{}) + (\underline{} \div \underline{})$

    $= \underline{} + \underline{} + \underline{} = $

- $615 \div 5 = (\underline{} \div \underline{}) + (\underline{} \div \underline{}) + (\underline{} \div \underline{})$

    $= \underline{} + \underline{} + \underline{} = $

C. Solve these problems **mentally** :

☐ A basket has 575 mangoes. If 5 mangoes cost a dollar, how many dollars can buy all the mangoes ?

_____ ÷ ___ = (_____ ÷ _____) + (_____ ÷ _____) + (_____ ÷ _____)

= _____ + _____ + _____ = [   ]

☐ Into how many sets of 5 each can 315 marbles be divided ?

_____ ÷ ___ = (_____ ÷ _____) + (_____ ÷ _____) + (_____ ÷ _____)

= _____ + _____ + _____ = [   ]

☐ 535 travellers reached an inn. If 5 travellers can stay in a room. How many rooms are needed for all the travellers ?

_____ ÷ ___ = (_____ ÷ _____) + (_____ ÷ _____) + (_____ ÷ _____)

= _____ + _____ + _____ = [   ]

☐ 1025 marbles are to be divided among children. If each child gets 5 marbles, how many children will take away all the marbles ?

_____ ÷ ___ = (_____ ÷ _____) + (_____ ÷ _____) + (_____ ÷ _____)

= _____ + _____ + _____ = [   ]

☐ 235 indoor patients reach a hospital for treatment. If a room can have 5 patients, how many rooms are needed for all the patients ?

_____ ÷ ___ = (_____ ÷ _____) + (_____ ÷ _____) + (_____ ÷ _____)

= _____ + _____ + _____ = [   ]

☐ 645 players reach a training camp. If 5 players can stay in a tent, how many tents will all the players occupy ?

_____ ÷ ___ = (_____ ÷ _____) + (_____ ÷ _____) + (_____ ÷ _____)

= _____ + _____ + _____ = [   ]

☐ 1575 guests reach a dining hall. If 5 guests can sit at a table, how many tables are needed for all the guests ?

_____ ÷ ___ = (_____ ÷ _____) + (_____ ÷ _____) + (_____ ÷ _____)

= _____ + _____ + _____ = [   ]

☐ Into how many groups of 5 each can 1545 soldiers be divided ?

_____ ÷ ___ = (_____ ÷ _____) + (_____ ÷ _____) + (_____ ÷ _____)

= _____ + _____ + _____ = [   ]

(35) DIVISION BY 6

- Observe the digit in the **one's place** of the given numeral, if it is divisible by 2 or not.
- Add the digits of the numeral to see if the sum is divisible by 3.
- If the numeral is divisible by 2 and 3, it is divisible by 6 also.

Can 636 be divided by 6 ?
The digit 6 in the one's place can be divided by 2. The sum of the digits 6, 3, 6 is 15 which is divisible by 3. So, 636 is divisible by 6.

$636 \div 6$
$= (600 \div 6) + (30 \div 6) + (6 \div 6)$
$= 100 + 5 + 1 = 106$

DO YOURSELF

A. Write **Yes** if the numeral can be divided by 6. If not, write **No** :

- ❑ Can 923 be divided by 6 ? _____
- ❑ Can 294 be divided by 6 ? _____
- ❑ Can 306 be divided by 6 ? _____
- ❑ Can 580 be divided by 6 ? _____
- ❑ Can 696 be divided by 6 ? _____
- ❑ Can 3366 be divided by 6 ? _____

B. Divide by **break-up** method :

- ❑ $336 \div 6$
  $= (300 \div 6) + (30 \div 6) + (6 \div 6) = 50 + 5 + 1 = \boxed{56}$

- ❑ $966 \div 6 = (\_\_\_\_ \div \_\_\_\_) + (\_\_\_\_ \div \_\_\_\_) + (\_\_\_\_ \div \_\_\_\_)$
  $= \_\_\_\_ + \_\_\_\_ + \_\_\_\_ =$

- ❑ $936 \div 6 = (\_\_\_ \div \_\_\_) + (\_\_\_ \div \_\_\_) + (\_\_\_ \div \_\_\_)$
  $= \_\_\_\_ + \_\_\_\_ + \_\_\_\_ =$

- ❑ $366 \div 6 = (\_\_\_ \div \_\_\_) + (\_\_\_ \div \_\_\_) + (\_\_\_ \div \_\_\_)$
  $= \_\_\_\_ + \_\_\_\_ + \_\_\_\_ =$

C. Solve these problems **mentally** :

❏ How many six-member families will 6336 people of a village make ?

_____ ÷ ___ = (_____ ÷ _____) + (_____ ÷ _____) + (_____ ÷ _____)

= _____ + _____ + _____ = [   ]

❏ A club has 6060 members. If each table can have 6 members, how many tables are required for all the members ?

_____ ÷ ___ = (_____ ÷ _____) + (_____ ÷ _____) + (_____ ÷ _____)

= _____ + _____ + _____ = [   ]

❏ 966 passengers are to cross a river by boat. If the boat can carry only 6 passengers, how many times will it cross the river for all passengers ?

_____ ÷ ___ = (_____ ÷ _____) + (_____ ÷ _____) + (_____ ÷ _____)

= _____ + _____ + _____ = [   ]

❏ 836 marbles are to be distributed among children. If each child gets 6 marbles, how many children will take away all the marbles ?

_____ ÷ ___ = (_____ ÷ _____) + (_____ ÷ _____) + (_____ ÷ _____)

= _____ + _____ + _____ = [   ]

❏ There are 6636 cattle in a fair. If each buyer buys 6 cattle, how many buyers will buy all the cattle ?

_____ ÷ ___ = (_____ ÷ _____) + (_____ ÷ _____) + (_____ ÷ _____)

= _____ + _____ + _____ = [   ]

❏ A basket has 6696 lychees. If each bunch has 6 lychees, find the number of bunches.

_____ ÷ ___ = (_____ ÷ _____) + (_____ ÷ _____) + (_____ ÷ _____)

= _____ + _____ + _____ = [   ]

❏ 3096 watermelons were put into baskets. If each basket contains 6 watermelons, find the number of baskets.

_____ ÷ ___ = (_____ ÷ _____) + (_____ ÷ _____) + (_____ ÷ _____)

= _____ + _____ + _____ = [   ]

❏ How many sets of 6 toffees each can 3336 toffees be made into ?

_____ ÷ ___ = (_____ ÷ _____) + (_____ ÷ _____) + (_____ ÷ _____)

= _____ + _____ + _____ = [   ]

(36) DIVISION BY 7

READ CAREFULLY

- Multiply the ones digit by 2 to get a product.
- Subtract this product from the numeral made by other digits.
- If the remainder is divisible by 7, the entire numeral can be divided by 7.

Can 441 be divided by 7 ?

One's digit is 1 and $1 \times 2 = 2$

Other digits make the numeral 44.

$44 - 2 = 42$ which is divisible by 7.

So 441 is also divisible by 7.

$441 \div 7$

$= (420 \div 7) + (21 \div 7)$

$= 60 + 3 = 63$

DO YOURSELF

A. Write **Yes** if the numeral can be divided by 7. If not, write **No** :

❏ Can 616 be divided by 7 ? _____

❏ Can 219 be divided by 7 ? _____

❏ Can 273 be divided by 7 ? _____

❏ Can 339 be divided by 7 ? _____

❏ Can 735 be divided by 7 ? _____

❏ Can 955 be divided by 7 ? _____

B. Divide by **break-up** method :

❏ $385 \div 7 = (350 \div 7) + (35 \div 7) = 50 + 5 = \boxed{55}$

❏ $679 \div 7 = (\_\_\_ \div \_\_\_) + (\_\_\_ \div \_\_\_) = \_\_\_ + \_\_\_ = \boxed{}$

❏ $945 \div 7 = (\_\_\_ \div \_\_\_) + (\_\_\_ \div \_\_\_) = \_\_\_ + \_\_\_ = \boxed{}$

❏ $952 \div 7 = (\_\_\_ \div \_\_\_) + (\_\_\_ \div \_\_\_) = \_\_\_ + \_\_\_ = \boxed{}$

❏ $392 \div 7 = (\_\_\_ \div \_\_\_) + (\_\_\_ \div \_\_\_) = \_\_\_ + \_\_\_ = \boxed{}$

❏ $798 \div 7 = (\_\_\_ \div \_\_\_) + (\_\_\_ \div \_\_\_) = \_\_\_ + \_\_\_ = \boxed{}$

❏ $504 \div 7 = (\_\_\_ \div \_\_\_) + (\_\_\_ \div \_\_\_) = \_\_\_ + \_\_\_ = \boxed{}$

C. Solve these problems **mentally** :

❏ A basket has 7735 oranges which are to be grouped in sets of 7 each. How many sets will be there in all ?

$7735 \div 7 = (7000 \div 7) + (700 \div 7) + (35 \div 7) = 1000 + 100 + 5 = 1105$

❏ There were 2793 guests at a party. If 7 guests can sit at a dining table. How many tables are needed for all the guests ?

____ ÷ __ = (_____ ÷ __) + (___ ÷ __) + (__ ÷ __) = ____ + __ + __ = ☐

❏ There were 3892 cattle in a fair. If a buyer buys 7 cattle, how many buyers will buy all the cattle ?

____ ÷ __ = (_____ ÷ __) + (___ ÷ __) + (__ ÷ __) = ____ + __ + __ = ☐

❏ 4494 passengers boarded a train. 7 passengers can sit on a berth. How many berths are needed for all the passengers ?

____ ÷ __ = (_____ ÷ __) + (___ ÷ __) + (__ ÷ __) = ____ + __ + __ = ☐

❏ A cart had 2254 watermelons loaded on it. 7 watermelons are sold for a dollar. How many dollars are needed to buy all the watermelons ?

____ ÷ __ = (_____ ÷ __) + (___ ÷ __) + (__ ÷ __) = ____ + __ + __ = ☐

❏ A school has 3493 students in all. If 7 students can sit on a bench, how many benches will be occupied by all the students ?

____ ÷ __ = (_____ ÷ __) + (___ ÷ __) + (__ ÷ __) = ____ + __ + __ = ☐

❏ There are 5082 toffees in a platter to be distributed among children. If each child gets 7 toffees, find the number of children.

____ ÷ __ = (_____ ÷ __) + (___ ÷ __) + (__ ÷ __) = ____ + __ + __ = ☐

❏ 5194 marbles are to be made into groups of 7 each. How many groups of marbles will there be in all ?

____ ÷ __ = (_____ ÷ __) + (___ ÷ __) + (__ ÷ __) = ____ + __ + __ = ☐

❏ 6237 passengers want to cross a river by boat. If a boat can carry 7 passengers, how many boats are required for them to cross the river ?

____ ÷ __ = (_____ ÷ __) + (___ ÷ __) + (__ ÷ __) = ____ + __ + __ = ☐

❏ How many bouquets of 7 flowers each will 5075 flowers make ?

____ ÷ __ = (_____ ÷ __) + (___ ÷ __) + (__ ÷ __) = ____ + __ + __ = ☐

(37) DIVISION BY 9

- Add up all the digits to get their sum.

- If the sum is divisible by 9, the entire numeral is divisible by 9.

- Division can be done by break-up method.

> **Can 252 be divided by 9 ?**
>
> The sum of the digits 2, 5, 2 = 9.
>
> It is divisible by 9.
>
> So 252 is also divisible by 9.
>
> $252 \div 9$
>
> $= (180 \div 9) + (45 \div 9) + (27 \div 9)$
>
> $= 20 + 5 + 3 = 28$

DO YOURSELF

A. Write **Yes** if the numeral can be divided by 7. If not, write **No** :

- ❏ Can 297 be divided by 9 ? _____

- ❏ Can 816 be divided by 9 ? _____

- ❏ Can 684 be divided by 9 ? _____

- ❏ Can 798 be divided by 9 ? _____

- ❏ Can 864 be divided by 9 ? _____

- ❏ Can 549 be divided by 9 ? _____

B. Divide by **break-up** method :

- ❏ $999 \div 9$

  $= (900 \div 9) + (90 \div 9) + (9 \div 9) = 100 + 10 + 1 = \boxed{111}$

- ❏ $738 \div 9$

  $= (\underline{} \div \underline{}) + (\underline{} \div \underline{}) + (\underline{} \div \underline{}) = \underline{} + \underline{} + \underline{} = \boxed{}$

- ❏ $882 \div 9$

  $= (\underline{} \div \underline{}) + (\underline{} \div \underline{}) + (\underline{} \div \underline{}) = \underline{} + \underline{} + \underline{} = \boxed{}$

- ❏ $504 \div 9$

  $= (\underline{} \div \underline{}) + (\underline{} \div \underline{}) + (\underline{} \div \underline{}) = \underline{} + \underline{} + \underline{} = \boxed{}$

C. Solve these problems mentally :

☐ 2547 biscuits are to be distributed among beggars. If each beggar gets 9 biscuits, find the total number of beggars.

$2547 \div 9 = (1800 \div 9) + (720 \div 9) + (27 \div 9) = 200 + 80 + 3 = \boxed{283}$

☐ 5076 trees are to be planted in a garden in rows. If each row has 9 trees, how many rows of trees will there be in all ?

_____ ÷ __ = (_____ ÷ __) + (___ ÷ __) + (__ ÷ __) = _____ + __ + __ = ☐

☐ 8253 passengers board a train. If 9 passengers can sit on each berth, find the total number of berths.

_____ ÷ __ = (_____ ÷ __) + (___ ÷ __) + (__ ÷ __) = _____ + __ + __ = ☐

☐ 2979 soldiers are organized in teams of 9 soldiers each. How many teams will be there in all ?

_____ ÷ __ = (_____ ÷ __) + (___ ÷ __) + (__ ÷ __) = _____ + __ + __ = ☐

☐ 9954 pumpkins were put in baskets. If each basket contains 9 pumpkins, find the total number of baskets.

_____ ÷ __ = (_____ ÷ __) + (___ ÷ __) + (__ ÷ __) = _____ + __ + __ = ☐

☐ 3492 players are to be made into groups of 9 players each. How many groups will there be in all ?

_____ ÷ __ = (_____ ÷ __) + (___ ÷ __) + (__ ÷ __) = _____ + __ + __ = ☐

☐ 8676 melons were loaded on a cart to be sold to customers. If each customer buys 9 melons, find the total number of customers.

_____ ÷ __ = (_____ ÷ __) + (___ ÷ __) + (__ ÷ __) = _____ + __ + __ = ☐

☐ 6858 guests came to attend a birthday feast. If 9 guests can sit at a table, how many tables are needed for all the guests ?

_____ ÷ __ = (_____ ÷ __) + (___ ÷ __) + (__ ÷ __) = _____ + __ + __ = ☐

☐ 7344 toffees are to be made into sets of 9 toffees each. How many sets of toffees will there be in all ?

_____ ÷ __ = (_____ ÷ __) + (___ ÷ __) + (__ ÷ __) = _____ + __ + __ = ☐

☐ 4428 marbles are to be made into sets of 9 each. Find the number of sets.

_____ ÷ __ = (_____ ÷ __) + (___ ÷ __) + (__ ÷ __) = _____ + __ + __ = ☐

38 DIVISION BY 11

READ CAREFULLY

- Add the digits in the alternate places to find their sums.
- Find the difference between the two sums.
- If the difference is 0 or divisible by 11, the numeral is divisible by 11.

Can 2475 be divided by 11 ?
$5 + 4 = 9$ and $7 + 2 = 9$
Their difference $= 9 - 9 = 0$
So 2475 is divisible by 11.
$$2475 \div 11$$
$$= (2200 \div 11) + (220 \div 11) + (55 \div 11)$$
$$= 200 + 20 + 5 = 225$$

DO YOURSELF

A. Write Yes if the numeral can be divided by 7. If not, write No :

- ❏ Can 231 be divided by 11 ? _____
- ❏ Can 384 be divided by 11 ? _____
- ❏ Can 594 be divided by 11 ? _____
- ❏ Can 9504 be divided by 11 ? _____
- ❏ Can 181 be divided by 11 ? _____
- ❏ Can 3795 be divided by 11 ? _____

B. Divide by break-up method :

- ❏ $4312 \div 11$
  $= (3300 \div 11) + (990 \div 11) + (22 \div 11) = 300 + 90 + 2 = \boxed{392}$
- ❏ $9273 \div 11$
  $= (\_\_\_\_ \div \_\_) + (\_\_\_\_ \div \_\_\_) + (\_\_\_ \div \_\_) = \_\_\_ + \_\_ + \_\_ = \boxed{}$
- ❏ $6721 \div 11$
  $= (\_\_\_\_ \div \_\_) + (\_\_\_\_ \div \_\_\_) + (\_\_\_ \div \_\_) = \_\_\_ + \_\_ + \_\_ = \boxed{}$
- ❏ $3883 \div 11$
  $= (\_\_\_\_ \div \_\_) + (\_\_\_\_ \div \_\_\_) + (\_\_\_ \div \_\_) = \_\_\_ + \_\_ + \_\_ = \boxed{}$

C. Solve these problems **mentally** :

❐ 7271 marbles are to be made into sets of 11 marbles each. Find the total number of sets.

$7271 \div 11 = (6600 \div 11) + (660 \div 11) + (11 \div 11) = 600 + 60 + 1 = \boxed{661}$

❐ 9757 trees are to be planted in rows in a garden. If each row has 11 trees, how many rows of trees will there be in all ?

_____ ÷ __ = (_____ ÷ __) + (___ ÷ __) + (__ ÷ __) = _____ + __ + __ = ☐

❐ 8932 passengers board a train. If 11 passengers can sit on a berth, how many berths are needed for all the passengers ?

_____ ÷ __ = (_____ ÷ __) + (___ ÷ __) + (__ ÷ __) = _____ + __ + __ = ☐

❐ 9262 cattle reached a fair to be sold. If each customer buys 11 cattle, how many customers will buy all the cattle ?

_____ ÷ __ = (_____ ÷ __) + (___ ÷ __) + (__ ÷ __) = _____ + __ + __ = ☐

❐ A school has 2321 students who are to be made into groups of 11 each. How many groups will there be in all ?

_____ ÷ __ = (_____ ÷ __) + (___ ÷ __) + (__ ÷ __) = _____ + __ + __ = ☐

❐ A cart has 6754 melons on it. They are to be put in baskets. If each basket has 11 melons. Find the total number of baskets.

_____ ÷ __ = (_____ ÷ __) + (___ ÷ __) + (__ ÷ __) = _____ + __ + __ = ☐

❐ 5951 passengers want to cross a river by boat. If a boat can carry 11 passengers, how many boats are required to take all the passengers across ?

_____ ÷ __ = (_____ ÷ __) + (___ ÷ __) + (__ ÷ __) = _____ + __ + __ = ☐

❐ There were 4653 guests at a party. If 11 guests can sit at a table, how many tables will all the guests occupy ?

_____ ÷ __ = (_____ ÷ __) + (___ ÷ __) + (__ ÷ __) = _____ + __ + __ = ☐

❐ 11 toffees can be bought with one dollar. How many dollars will have to be spent to buy 7821 toffees ?

_____ ÷ __ = (_____ ÷ __) + (___ ÷ __) + (__ ÷ __) = _____ + __ + __ = ☐

❐ How many bouquets with 11 flowers each can be made with 2178 flowers ?

_____ ÷ __ = (_____ ÷ __) + (___ ÷ __) + (__ ÷ __) = _____ + __ + __ = ☐

㉟ SIMPLE FRACTIONS

- A fraction means a part of a whole.

- While writing a fraction in words, the parts taken are written first.

- The total number of parts of the whole are written as ordinals later on.

- Observe the fractions written and shown with diagrams

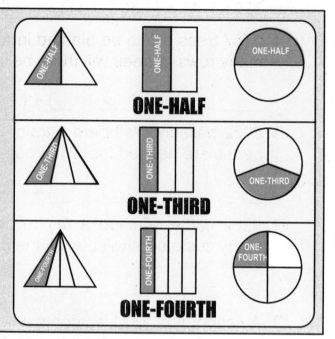

ONE-HALF

ONE-THIRD

ONE-FOURTH

DO YOURSELF

A. Shade each figure according to the **fraction** :

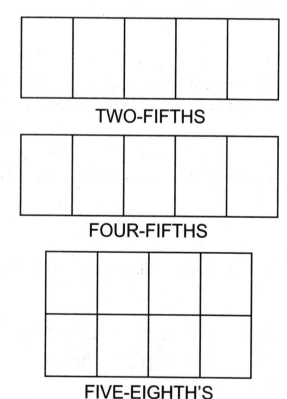

TWO-FIFTHS

FOUR-FIFTHS

FIVE-EIGHTH'S

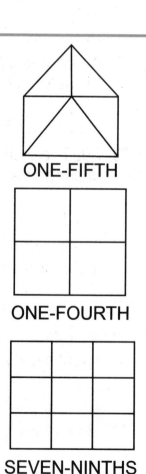

ONE-FIFTH

ONE-FOURTH

SEVEN-NINTHS

B. Name the shaded part as a **fraction** in words :

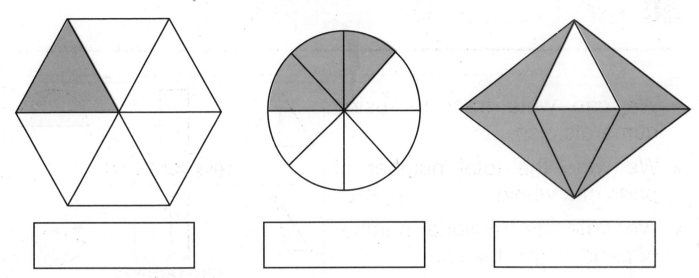

C. Name the unshaded part as a **fraction** in words :

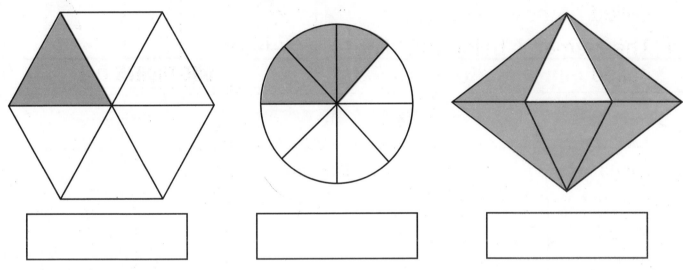

D. Answer :

1. What is meant by a fraction ?

    _____

2. How many parts has a fraction ?

    _____

3. Which part of a fraction is written first ?

    _____

4. Which part of a fraction is written later on ?

    _____

READ CAREFULLY

- We can write fractions using numerals also.
- We write the total number of parts of a whole below the line.
- We write the fractional number of parts above the line.
- The numeral above the line is called numerator.
- The numeral below the line is called denominator.

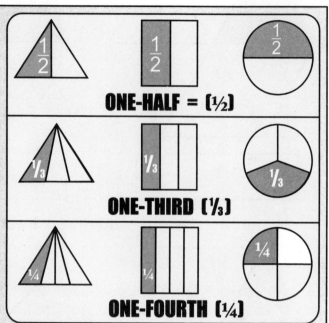

ONE-HALF = (½)

ONE-THIRD (⅓)

ONE-FOURTH (¼)

DO YOURSELF

A. Shade each figure according to the **fraction** :

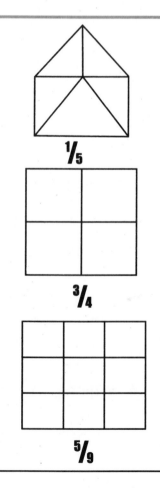

³/₅

²/₅

⁵/₈

¹/₅

³/₄

⁵/₉

B. Name the shaded part as a fraction in numerals :

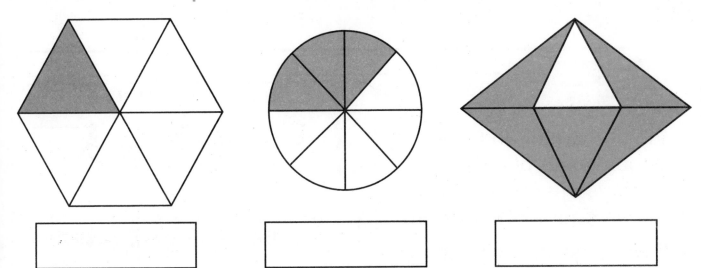

C. Name the unshaded part as a fraction in numerals :

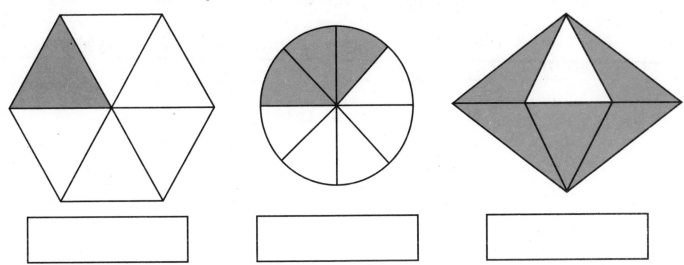

D. Write in numerals each fraction given in words :

1. Four-fifths _____   2. Two-thirds _____

3. Four-ninths _____   4. Two-fifths _____

5. Three-fourths _____   6. Seven-eighths _____

7. One-fourth _____   8. Five-sixths _____

9. Three-sevenths _____   10. Eight-ninths _____

11. Five-sixths _____   12. Four-sevenths _____

13. One-third _____   14. Three-eighths _____

(41) EQUIVALENT FRACTIONS

READ CAREFULLY

- If we multiply or divide both the numerator and the denominator of a fraction by the same numeral, we get an equivalent fraction.

- If we cross multiply the parts of equivalent fractions the products are the same.

- We can check this fact as shown in front.

EQUIVALENT FRACTIONS

$$\frac{1}{2} = \frac{2}{4} = \frac{3}{6} = \frac{4}{8} = \frac{5}{10} = \frac{6}{12}$$

CROSS MULTIPLICATION

$\frac{1}{2} \times \frac{2}{4}$ product = 4. $\frac{1}{2} \times \frac{3}{6}$ product = 6.

$\frac{2}{4} \times \frac{3}{6}$ product = 12. $\frac{1}{4} \times \frac{2}{8}$ product = 8.

$\frac{3}{6} \times \frac{4}{8}$ product = 24. $\frac{4}{8} \times \frac{5}{10}$ product = 40.

DO YOURSELF

A. Write four equivalent fractions for each given fractions :

$\frac{1}{3}$ = _____ _____ _____ _____

$\frac{1}{4}$ = _____ _____ _____ _____

$\frac{1}{5}$ = _____ _____ _____ _____

$\frac{2}{3}$ = _____ _____ _____ _____

$\frac{3}{4}$ = _____ _____ _____ _____

$\frac{5}{6}$ = _____ _____ _____ _____

$\frac{6}{7}$ = _____ _____ _____ _____

B. Check the equivalent fractions by cross-multiplication :

☐ $\frac{1}{3} = \frac{2}{6}$, product = _____   ☐ $\frac{1}{4} = \frac{3}{12}$ product = _____

☐ $\frac{1}{5} = \frac{5}{25}$, product = _____   ☐ $\frac{2}{3} = \frac{6}{9}$ product = _____

☐ $\frac{3}{4} = \frac{12}{16}$, product = _____   ☐ $\frac{3}{5} = \frac{9}{15}$ product = _____

☐ $\frac{2}{5} = \frac{8}{20}$, product = _____   ☐ $\frac{5}{6} = \frac{20}{24}$ product = _____

☐ $\frac{3}{7} = \frac{12}{28}$, product = _____   ☐ $\frac{6}{7} = \frac{18}{21}$ product = _____

C. Write each fraction in its lowest form :

☐ $\frac{8}{10}$ = _____   ☐ $\frac{6}{8}$ = _____   ☐ $\frac{16}{20}$ = _____

☐ $\frac{8}{12}$ = _____   ☐ $\frac{9}{15}$ = _____   ☐ $\frac{18}{21}$ = _____

☐ $\frac{4}{14}$ = _____   ☐ $\frac{6}{18}$ = _____   ☐ $\frac{21}{27}$ = _____

☐ $\frac{24}{28}$ = _____   ☐ $\frac{9}{30}$ = _____   ☐ $\frac{14}{18}$ = _____

☐ $\frac{20}{28}$ = _____   ☐ $\frac{15}{27}$ = _____   ☐ $\frac{35}{49}$ = _____

☐ $\frac{28}{32}$ = _____   ☐ $\frac{32}{44}$ = _____   ☐ $\frac{9}{21}$ = _____

☐ $\frac{21}{35}$ = _____   ☐ $\frac{22}{33}$ = _____   ☐ $\frac{28}{36}$ = _____

☐ $\frac{5}{20}$ = _____   ☐ $\frac{6}{42}$ = _____   ☐ $\frac{21}{56}$ = _____

☐ $\frac{27}{36}$ = _____   ☐ $\frac{45}{54}$ = _____   ☐ $\frac{54}{63}$ = _____

☐ $\frac{72}{81}$ = _____   ☐ $\frac{63}{90}$ = _____   ☐ $\frac{45}{55}$ = _____

D. Write the suitable numerator / denominator to make the fractions equivalent :

$\frac{5}{7} = \frac{\bigcirc}{21}$	$\frac{8}{9} = \frac{24}{\bigcirc}$	$\frac{\bigcirc}{30} = \frac{7}{15}$
$\frac{5}{\bigcirc} = \frac{25}{55}$	$\frac{\bigcirc}{24} = \frac{5}{6}$	$\frac{5}{\bigcirc} = \frac{35}{84}$
$\frac{7}{13} = \frac{\bigcirc}{39}$	$\frac{1}{8} = \frac{8}{\bigcirc}$	$\frac{\bigcirc}{48} = \frac{7}{16}$
$\frac{11}{\bigcirc} = \frac{22}{26}$	$\frac{\bigcirc}{9} = \frac{42}{54}$	$\frac{30}{\bigcirc} = \frac{15}{17}$
$\frac{8}{9} = \frac{\bigcirc}{45}$	$\frac{\bigcirc}{17} = \frac{28}{68}$	$\frac{\bigcirc}{75} = \frac{13}{15}$
$\frac{6}{\bigcirc} = \frac{18}{21}$	$\frac{7}{17} = \frac{49}{\bigcirc}$	$\frac{110}{\bigcirc} = \frac{11}{17}$
$\frac{11}{13} = \frac{\bigcirc}{52}$	$\frac{19}{50} = \frac{38}{\bigcirc}$	$\frac{\bigcirc}{54} = \frac{5}{9}$
$\frac{\bigcirc}{100} = \frac{3}{10}$	$\frac{\bigcirc}{40} = \frac{38}{80}$	$\frac{3}{4} = \frac{9}{\bigcirc}$

42 RECIPROCALS

READ CAREFULLY

- The word—reciprocal—means **reverse**.

- The reciprocal of a fraction is got by changing the places of its numerator and denominator.

FRACTION	RECIPROCAL
$\frac{2}{3}$	$\frac{3}{2}$
$\frac{5}{3}$	$\frac{3}{5}$
5	$\frac{1}{5}$

DO YOURSELF

A. Write the reciprocals of :

☐ $\frac{5}{7}$ ⟶ [ ]   ☐ $\frac{3}{5}$ ⟶ [ ]

☐ $\frac{4}{21}$ ⟶ [ ]   ☐ $\frac{2}{9}$ ⟶ [ ]

☐ $\frac{4}{13}$ ⟶ [ ]   ☐ 7 ⟶ [ ]

☐ $\frac{3}{8}$ ⟶ [ ]   ☐ $\frac{4}{5}$ ⟶ [ ]

☐ $\frac{1}{9}$ ⟶ [ ]   ☐ $\frac{2}{3}$ ⟶ [ ]

☐ $\frac{5}{9}$ ⟶ [ ]   ☐ $\frac{5}{8}$ ⟶ [ ]

☐ $\frac{8}{9}$ ⟶ [ ]   ☐ $\frac{1}{8}$ ⟶ [ ]

☐ 5 ⟶ [ ]   ☐ $\frac{1}{6}$ ⟶ [ ]

READ CAREFULLY

- If two fractions have the same numerator, the fraction with the **lower denominator** is **higher** than the other.

$\frac{1}{2}$	$\frac{1}{3}$	$\frac{1}{4}$
highest	**lower**	**lowest**

- If two fractions have the same denominator, the fraction with the **higher numerator** is **higher** than the other.

$\frac{1}{5}$	$\frac{3}{5}$	$\frac{4}{5}$
lowest	**higher**	**highest**

DO YOURSELF

A. Put the sign greater than **(>)** or **(<)** less than between each pair of fractions :

- $\frac{1}{2}$ ☐ $\frac{1}{3}$
- $\frac{1}{4}$ ☐ $\frac{1}{3}$
- $\frac{3}{5}$ ☐ $\frac{3}{7}$

- $\frac{2}{5}$ ☐ $\frac{3}{7}$
- $\frac{4}{5}$ ☐ $\frac{4}{9}$
- $\frac{4}{7}$ ☐ $\frac{4}{9}$

- $\frac{5}{6}$ ☐ $\frac{5}{8}$
- $\frac{4}{5}$ ☐ $\frac{4}{7}$
- $\frac{1}{6}$ ☐ $\frac{1}{9}$

- $\frac{1}{13}$ ☐ $\frac{1}{15}$
- $\frac{1}{8}$ ☐ $\frac{1}{5}$
- $\frac{4}{11}$ ☐ $\frac{4}{9}$

- $\frac{11}{17}$ ☐ $\frac{11}{13}$
- $\frac{2}{7}$ ☐ $\frac{2}{10}$
- $\frac{7}{15}$ ☐ $\frac{7}{12}$

- $\frac{7}{9}$ ☐ $\frac{7}{12}$
- $\frac{6}{13}$ ☐ $\frac{6}{17}$
- $\frac{7}{11}$ ☐ $\frac{7}{12}$

B. Put the sign greater than **(>)** or **(<)** less than between each pair of fractions :

- $\frac{1}{4}$ ☐ $\frac{3}{4}$
- $\frac{2}{3}$ ☐ $\frac{1}{3}$
- $\frac{1}{5}$ ☐ $\frac{4}{5}$

- $\frac{2}{5}$ ☐ $\frac{3}{5}$
- $\frac{5}{6}$ ☐ $\frac{1}{6}$
- $\frac{2}{7}$ ☐ $\frac{4}{7}$

□ $\frac{5}{8}$ ☐ $\frac{3}{8}$ □ $\frac{8}{11}$ ☐ $\frac{5}{11}$ □ $\frac{10}{17}$ ☐ $\frac{13}{17}$

□ $\frac{5}{9}$ ☐ $\frac{4}{9}$ □ $\frac{9}{11}$ ☐ $\frac{8}{11}$ □ $\frac{5}{12}$ ☐ $\frac{7}{12}$

□ $\frac{7}{10}$ ☐ $\frac{3}{10}$ □ $\frac{10}{21}$ ☐ $\frac{11}{21}$ □ $\frac{11}{15}$ ☐ $\frac{13}{15}$

□ $\frac{11}{20}$ ☐ $\frac{9}{20}$ □ $\frac{9}{14}$ ☐ $\frac{3}{14}$ □ $\frac{7}{19}$ ☐ $\frac{13}{19}$

C.   Write the following fractions in **ascending order** :

□ $\frac{1}{2}$, $\frac{1}{3}$, $\frac{1}{4}$, $\frac{1}{5}$, $\frac{1}{6}$, $\frac{1}{7}$

_____

□ $\frac{7}{9}$, $\frac{7}{12}$, $\frac{7}{11}$, $\frac{7}{9}$, $\frac{7}{8}$, $\frac{7}{10}$

_____

□ $\frac{5}{13}$, $\frac{5}{7}$, $\frac{5}{11}$, $\frac{5}{9}$, $\frac{5}{7}$, $\frac{5}{6}$

_____

D.   Write the following fractions in **descending order** :

□ $\frac{1}{9}$, $\frac{4}{9}$, $\frac{2}{9}$, $\frac{5}{9}$, $\frac{7}{9}$, $\frac{8}{9}$

_____

□ $\frac{3}{7}$, $\frac{1}{7}$, $\frac{2}{7}$, $\frac{5}{7}$, $\frac{4}{7}$, $\frac{6}{7}$

_____

□ $\frac{2}{13}$, $\frac{5}{13}$, $\frac{3}{13}$, $\frac{8}{13}$, $\frac{9}{13}$, $\frac{4}{13}$

_____

44 ADDING LIKE FRACTIONS

READ CAREFULLY

- Fractions with the **same denominator** are called like fractions.
- Add the numerators to get the numerator of

$$\frac{1}{7} + \frac{5}{7}$$
$$= \frac{1+5}{7} = \frac{6}{7}$$

DO YOURSELF

A. Find the sum mentally :

☐ $\frac{1}{5} + \frac{1}{5}$

☐ $\frac{3}{8} + \frac{2}{8}$

☐ $\frac{2}{7} + \frac{3}{7}$

☐ $\frac{1}{7} + \frac{3}{7}$

☐ $\frac{2}{9} + \frac{3}{9}$

☐ $\frac{1}{5} + \frac{3}{5}$

☐ $\frac{1}{9} + \frac{4}{9}$

☐ $\frac{2}{9} + \frac{5}{9}$

☐ $\frac{5}{8} + \frac{2}{8}$

☐ $\frac{2}{5} + \frac{2}{5}$

☐ $\frac{3}{11} + \frac{2}{11}$

☐ $\frac{4}{11} + \frac{3}{11}$

☐ $\frac{5}{11} + \frac{2}{11}$

☐ $\frac{2}{13} + \frac{7}{13}$

☐ $\frac{1}{15} + \frac{7}{15}$

☐ $\frac{4}{15} + \frac{7}{15}$

READ CAREFULLY

- Fractions with **different denominators** are called unlike fractions.
- Change the fraction with the lower denominator into an equivalent fraction with the same denominator as of the other fraction.
- Then add them like fractions.

Add $\dfrac{4}{9} + \dfrac{1}{3}$

$\dfrac{1}{3} = \dfrac{3}{9}$ (Equivalent Fraction)

So $\dfrac{4}{9} + \dfrac{1}{3} = \dfrac{4}{9} + \dfrac{3}{9}$

$= \dfrac{4+3}{9} = \dfrac{7}{9}$

DO YOURSELF

A. Find the sum mentally :

☐ $\dfrac{1}{5} + \dfrac{4}{15}$ ☐ ☐ $\dfrac{1}{8} + \dfrac{3}{4}$

☐ $\dfrac{1}{6} + \dfrac{2}{3}$ ☐ ☐ $\dfrac{1}{4} + \dfrac{1}{2}$

☐ $\dfrac{3}{10} + \dfrac{2}{5}$ ☐ ☐ $\dfrac{3}{7} + \dfrac{5}{14}$

☐ $\dfrac{2}{5} + \dfrac{7}{15}$ ☐ ☐ $\dfrac{5}{8} + \dfrac{3}{16}$

☐ $\dfrac{4}{9} + \dfrac{1}{36}$ ☐ ☐ $\dfrac{1}{3} + \dfrac{7}{12}$

☐ $\dfrac{1}{9} + \dfrac{11}{18}$ ☐ ☐ $\dfrac{1}{6} + \dfrac{19}{36}$

☐ $\dfrac{3}{4} + \dfrac{3}{16}$ ☐ ☐ $\dfrac{1}{3} + \dfrac{5}{9}$

READ CAREFULLY

- Add the denominators and multiply the sum with the common numerator.
- The product will be the numerator of the sum.
- Multiply the denominators to get the denominator of the sum.

Add : $\frac{1}{12} + \frac{1}{5}$

$(12 + 5) \times 1 = 17$ (numerator)

$12 \times 5 = 60$ (denominator)

So $\frac{1}{12} + \frac{1}{5} = \frac{17}{60}$

DO YOURSELF

A. Find the sum mentally :

☐ $\frac{1}{5} + \frac{1}{7}$ ☐

☐ $\frac{2}{7} + \frac{2}{5}$ ☐

☐ $\frac{3}{5} + \frac{3}{8}$ ☐

☐ $\frac{1}{8} + \frac{1}{9}$ ☐

☐ $\frac{4}{5} + \frac{4}{7}$ ☐

☐ $\frac{5}{7} + \frac{5}{8}$ ☐

☐ $\frac{2}{3} + \frac{2}{5}$ ☐

☐ $\frac{3}{4} + \frac{3}{7}$ ☐

☐ $\frac{6}{7} + \frac{6}{11}$ ☐

☐ $\frac{7}{9} + \frac{7}{8}$ ☐

☐ $\frac{5}{8} + \frac{5}{9}$ ☐

☐ $\frac{1}{5} + \frac{1}{6}$ ☐

☐ $\frac{1}{7} + \frac{1}{8}$ ☐

☐ $\frac{1}{8} + \frac{1}{9}$ ☐

☐ $\frac{3}{5} + \frac{3}{4}$ ☐

☐ $\frac{3}{8} + \frac{3}{7}$ ☐

READ CAREFULLY

- Take the difference between the denominators and multiply it by the same numerator.
- The product will be the numerator of the remainder.
- Multiply the denominators to get the denominators of the remainder.

Subtract : $\dfrac{3}{5} - \dfrac{3}{10}$

Numerator of the remainder.
$= (10 - 5) \times 3 = 5 \times 3 = 15$

Denominator of the remainder
$5 \times 10 = 50$

$\dfrac{3}{5} - \dfrac{3}{10} = \dfrac{15}{50} = \dfrac{3}{10}$

DO YOURSELF

A. **Find the sum mentally :**

- $\dfrac{1}{5} - \dfrac{1}{10}$ ☐

- $\dfrac{2}{9} - \dfrac{2}{11}$ ☐

- $\dfrac{3}{5} - \dfrac{3}{8}$ ☐

- $\dfrac{1}{7} - \dfrac{1}{9}$ ☐

- $\dfrac{2}{5} - \dfrac{2}{7}$ ☐

- $\dfrac{2}{5} - \dfrac{2}{7}$ ☐

- $\dfrac{2}{5} - \dfrac{2}{7}$ ☐

- $\dfrac{1}{6} - \dfrac{1}{7}$ ☐

- $\dfrac{1}{2} - \dfrac{1}{12}$ ☐

- $\dfrac{3}{5} - \dfrac{3}{7}$ ☐

- $\dfrac{3}{4} - \dfrac{3}{11}$ ☐

- $\dfrac{2}{3} - \dfrac{2}{5}$ ☐

- $\dfrac{2}{5} - \dfrac{2}{9}$ ☐

- $\dfrac{1}{3} - \dfrac{1}{11}$ ☐

- $\dfrac{3}{4} - \dfrac{1}{12}$ ☐

- $\dfrac{3}{4} - \dfrac{3}{7}$ ☐

- Take the difference between the numerators of the fractions.

- The difference will be the **numerator** of the remainder.

- The same denominator will be the denominator of the remainder.

Subtract : $\dfrac{5}{7} - \dfrac{3}{7}$

Numerator of the remainder
$= 5 - 3 = 2$

Denominator of the remainder $= 7$

So $\dfrac{5}{7} - \dfrac{3}{7} = \dfrac{5-3}{7} = \dfrac{2}{7}$

DO YOURSELF

A. Solve the following sum mentally :

☐ $\dfrac{4}{5} - \dfrac{1}{5}$ ☐ $\dfrac{7}{8} - \dfrac{5}{8}$

☐ $\dfrac{3}{5} - \dfrac{2}{5}$ ☐ $\dfrac{9}{11} - \dfrac{7}{11}$

☐ $\dfrac{11}{12} - \dfrac{7}{12}$ ☐ $\dfrac{7}{10} - \dfrac{3}{10}$

☐ $\dfrac{17}{20} - \dfrac{13}{20}$ ☐ $\dfrac{9}{13} - \dfrac{5}{13}$

☐ $\dfrac{11}{17} - \dfrac{7}{17}$ ☐ $\dfrac{11}{16} - \dfrac{9}{16}$

☐ $\dfrac{17}{21} - \dfrac{11}{21}$ ☐ $\dfrac{7}{22} - \dfrac{5}{22}$

☐ $\dfrac{9}{13} - \dfrac{5}{13}$ ☐ $\dfrac{11}{19} - \dfrac{7}{19}$

☐ $\dfrac{11}{18} - \dfrac{7}{18}$ ☐ $\dfrac{17}{20} - \dfrac{13}{20}$

49 SUBTRACTION OF UNLIKE FRACTIONS

READ CAREFULLY

- Unlike fractions have unlike denominators.
- Change the fraction with the lower denominator into an **equivalent fraction** with the same denominator as of the other fraction.
- Then subtract them as like fractions.

Subtract: $\dfrac{4}{9} - \dfrac{1}{3}$

$\dfrac{1}{3} = \dfrac{3}{9}$ (Equivalent fraction)

So $\dfrac{4}{9} - \dfrac{1}{3} = \dfrac{4}{9} - \dfrac{3}{9}$

$= \dfrac{4-3}{9} = \dfrac{1}{9}$

DO YOURSELF

A. Solve the following sum **mentally** :

▢ $\dfrac{2}{3} - \dfrac{1}{6}$

▢ $\dfrac{2}{5} - \dfrac{3}{10}$

▢ $\dfrac{7}{15} - \dfrac{2}{5}$

▢ $\dfrac{7}{9} - \dfrac{19}{27}$

▢ $\dfrac{5}{7} - \dfrac{13}{21}$

▢ $\dfrac{5}{6} - \dfrac{11}{18}$

▢ $\dfrac{5}{7} - \dfrac{19}{28}$

▢ $\dfrac{2}{3} - \dfrac{7}{15}$

▢ $\dfrac{7}{11} - \dfrac{9}{22}$

▢ $\dfrac{4}{5} - \dfrac{7}{10}$

▢ $\dfrac{5}{6} - \dfrac{23}{30}$

▢ $\dfrac{3}{4} - \dfrac{11}{16}$

▢ $\dfrac{1}{2} - \dfrac{3}{10}$

▢ $\dfrac{3}{4} - \dfrac{5}{8}$

▢ $\dfrac{4}{5} - \dfrac{8}{25}$

▢ $\dfrac{7}{8} - \dfrac{5}{24}$

READ CAREFULLY

- Multiply the digits other than zero (0) to get a product.

- Put the total number of the zeroes to the right of the product.

40×40

$= 4 \times 4 = 16$

Putting 2 zeroes to the right, we get = 1600

So $40 \times 40 = 1600$

DO YOURSELF

A. Find the products mentally :

☐ 10×10 = ☐

☐ 20×20 = ☐

☐ 30×30 = ☐

☐ 50×50 = ☐

☐ 60×60 = ☐

☐ 70×70 = ☐

☐ 80×80 = ☐

☐ 90×90 = ☐

☐ 100×100 = ☐

☐ 110×110 = ☐

A. Find the products mentally :

☐ 20×30 = ☐

☐ 10×20 = ☐

☐ 30×40 = ☐

☐ 40×50 = ☐

☐ 50×60 = ☐

☐ 60×70 = ☐

☐ 70×80 = ☐

☐ 80×90 = ☐

☐ 90×100 = ☐

☐ 100×110 = ☐

51 SQUARING ODD NUMERALS

- Subtract 1 from the odd numeral to get a **remainder**.
- Find the **square** of the remainder.
- Add up the **square**, the **remainder** and the **odd number** itself.

Find 7×7.

$7 - 1 = 6$ (remainder)

$6 \times 6 = 36$ (square)

So 7×7

$= 36 + 6 + 7 = 49$

DO YOURSELF

A. Find the squares **mentally** :

❏ $3 \times 3 = (2 \times 2) + 2 + 3 = 4 + 2 + 3 = \boxed{9}$

❏ $5 \times 5 \ = (\underline{\quad} \times \underline{\quad}) + \underline{\quad} + \underline{\quad} = \underline{\quad} + \underline{\quad} + \underline{\quad} = \boxed{}$

❏ $9 \times 9 \ = (\underline{\quad} \times \underline{\quad}) + \underline{\quad} + \underline{\quad} = \underline{\quad} + \underline{\quad} + \underline{\quad} = \boxed{}$

❏ $11 \times 11 \ = (\underline{\quad} \times \underline{\quad}) + \underline{\quad} + \underline{\quad} = \underline{\quad} + \underline{\quad} + \underline{\quad} = \boxed{}$

❏ $13 \times 13 \ = (\underline{\quad} \times \underline{\quad}) + \underline{\quad} + \underline{\quad} = \underline{\quad} + \underline{\quad} + \underline{\quad} = \boxed{}$

❏ $15 \times 15 \ = (\underline{\quad} \times \underline{\quad}) + \underline{\quad} + \underline{\quad} = \underline{\quad} + \underline{\quad} + \underline{\quad} = \boxed{}$

❏ $17 \times 17 \ = (\underline{\quad} \times \underline{\quad}) + \underline{\quad} + \underline{\quad} = \underline{\quad} + \underline{\quad} + \underline{\quad} = \boxed{}$

❏ $19 \times 19 \ = (\underline{\quad} \times \underline{\quad}) + \underline{\quad} + \underline{\quad} = \underline{\quad} + \underline{\quad} + \underline{\quad} = \boxed{}$

❏ $1 \times 1 \ = (\underline{\quad} \times \underline{\quad}) + \underline{\quad} + \underline{\quad} = \underline{\quad} + \underline{\quad} + \underline{\quad} = \boxed{}$

❏ $21 \times 21 \ = (\underline{\quad} \times \underline{\quad}) + \underline{\quad} + \underline{\quad} = \underline{\quad} + \underline{\quad} + \underline{\quad} = \boxed{}$

52 SQUARING EVEN NUMERALS

READ CAREFULLY

- Divide the numeral by 2 to get a **quotient**.

- **Square** the quotient.

- Multiply the square by 4.

Find 4×4.

$4 \div 2 = 2$ (quotient)

$2 \times 2 = 4$ (square)

So $4 \times 4 = 4 \times 4 = 16$

DO YOURSELF

A. Find the squares mentally :

☐ $2 \times 2 = (1 \times 1) \times 4 = \boxed{4}$

☐ $6 \times 6 = (\underline{\hspace{2cm}} \times \underline{\hspace{2cm}}) \times \underline{\hspace{2cm}} = $

☐ $8 \times 8 = (\underline{\hspace{2cm}} \times \underline{\hspace{2cm}}) \times \underline{\hspace{2cm}} = $

☐ $10 \times 10 = (\underline{\hspace{2cm}} \times \underline{\hspace{2cm}}) \times \underline{\hspace{2cm}} = $

☐ $12 \times 12 = (\underline{\hspace{2cm}} \times \underline{\hspace{2cm}}) \times \underline{\hspace{2cm}} = $

☐ $14 \times 14 = (\underline{\hspace{2cm}} \times \underline{\hspace{2cm}}) \times \underline{\hspace{2cm}} = $

☐ $16 \times 16 = (\underline{\hspace{2cm}} \times \underline{\hspace{2cm}}) \times \underline{\hspace{2cm}} = $

☐ $18 \times 18 = (\underline{\hspace{2cm}} \times \underline{\hspace{2cm}}) \times \underline{\hspace{2cm}} = $

☐ $20 \times 20 = (\underline{\hspace{2cm}} \times \underline{\hspace{2cm}}) \times \underline{\hspace{2cm}} = $

☐ $22 \times 22 = (\underline{\hspace{2cm}} \times \underline{\hspace{2cm}}) \times \underline{\hspace{2cm}} = $

READ CAREFULLY

- **Subtract 1** from the numeral.
- Multiply the remainder by **2** to get a **product**.
- Find the **square** of the remainder.
- Add up the **square**, the **product** and **1**.

Find 11 × 11.
11 − 1 = **10** remainder
10 × 2 = 20 product
10 × 10 = 100 square
So 11 × 11
= 100 + 20 + 1 = 121

DO YOURSELF

A. Find the squares mentally :

❐ 21 × 21   = (20 × 2) + (20 × 20) + 1 = 40 + 400 + 1 = **441**

❐ 31 × 31   = (___ × ___) + (___ × ___) + ___ = ___ + ___ + ___ =

❐ 41 × 41   = (___ × ___) + (___ × ___) + ___ = ___ + ___ + ___ =

❐ 51 × 51   = (___ × ___) + (___ × ___) + ___ = ___ + ___ + ___ =

❐ 61 × 61   = (___ × ___) + (___ × ___) + ___ = ___ + ___ + ___ =

❐ 71 × 71   = (___ × ___) + (___ × ___) + ___ = ___ + ___ + ___ =

❐ 81 × 81   = (___ × ___) + (___ × ___) + ___ = ___ + ___ + ___ =

❐ 91 × 91   = (___ × ___) + (___ × ___) + ___ = ___ + ___ + ___ =

❐ 101 × 101 = (___ × ___) + (___ × ___) + ___ = ___ + ___ + ___ =

❐ 111 × 111 = (___ × ___) + (___ × ___) + ___ = ___ + ___ + ___ =

54 SQUARING NUMERALS ENDING IN 2

READ CAREFULLY

- **Subtract 2** from the given numeral.
- Multiply the remainder by **4** to get a **product**.
- Find the **square** of the remainder.
- Add up the **square**, the **product** and **4**.

Find 12×12.
$12 - 2 = 10$ remainder
$10 \times 4 = 40$ product
$10 \times 10 = 100$ square
So 12×12
$= 100 + 40 + 4 = 144$

DO YOURSELF

A. Find the squares mentally :

❏ $22 \times 22 = (20 \times 4) + (20 \times 20) + 4 = 80 + 400 + 4 = \boxed{484}$

❏ $32 \times 32 = (__ \times __) + (__ \times __) + __ = __ + __ + __ = $

❏ $42 \times 42 = (__ \times __) + (__ \times __) + __ = __ + __ + __ = $

❏ $52 \times 52 = (__ \times __) + (__ \times __) + __ = __ + __ + __ = $

❏ $62 \times 62 = (__ \times __) + (__ \times __) + __ = __ + __ + __ = $

❏ $72 \times 72 = (__ \times __) + (__ \times __) + __ = __ + __ + __ = $

❏ $82 \times 82 = (__ \times __) + (__ \times __) + __ = __ + __ + __ = $

❏ $92 \times 92 = (__ \times __) + (__ \times __) + __ = __ + __ + __ = $

❏ $102 \times 102 = (__ \times __) + (__ \times __) + __ = __ + __ + __ = $

❏ $112 \times 112 = (__ \times __) + (__ \times __) + __ = __ + __ + __ = $

READ CAREFULLY

- **Subtract 3** from the given numeral.
- Multiply the remainder by **6** to get a **product**.
- Find the **square** of the remainder.
- Add up the **square**, the **product** and **9**.

Find 13 × 13.
13 − 3 = **10** remainder
10 × 6 = **60** product
10 × 10 = **100** square
So 13 × 13
= 100 + 60 + 9 = **169**

DO YOURSELF

A. Find the squares mentally :

❐ 23 × 23   = (20 × 6) + (20 × 20) + 9 = 120 + 400 + 9 = **529**

❐ 33 × 33   = (___ × ___) + (___ × ___) + ___ = ___ + ___ + ___ = [ ]

❐ 43 × 43   = (___ × ___) + (___ × ___) + ___ = ___ + ___ + ___ = [ ]

❐ 53 × 53   = (___ × ___) + (___ × ___) + ___ = ___ + ___ + ___ = [ ]

❐ 63 × 63   = (___ × ___) + (___ × ___) + ___ = ___ + ___ + ___ = [ ]

❐ 73 × 73   = (___ × ___) + (___ × ___) + ___ = ___ + ___ + ___ = [ ]

❐ 83 × 83   = (___ × ___) + (___ × ___) + ___ = ___ + ___ + ___ = [ ]

❐ 93 × 93   = (___ × ___) + (___ × ___) + ___ = ___ + ___ + ___ = [ ]

❐ 103 × 103 = (___ × ___) + (___ × ___) + ___ = ___ + ___ + ___ = [ ]

❐ 113 × 113 = (___ × ___) + (___ × ___) + ___ = ___ + ___ + ___ = [ ]

56 SQUARING NUMERALS ENDING IN 5

- **Double** the given numeral.
- You will get a numeral ending in zero.
- Find the **square** of the numeral ending in **0**.
- Divide the **square** by **4**.

Find 5×5.
$5 \times 2 = 10$ product
$10 \times 10 = 100$ square
So 5×5
$= 100 \div 4 = 25$

DO YOURSELF

A. Find the squares **mentally** :

❐ $15 \times 15 = (30 \times 30) = 900 \div 4 = \boxed{225}$

❐ $25 \times 25 = (___ \times _____) = (_____ \div _____) = $

❐ $35 \times 35 = (___ \times _____) = (_____ \div _____) = $

❐ $45 \times 45 = (___ \times _____) = (_____ \div _____) = $

❐ $55 \times 55 = (___ \times _____) = (_____ \div _____) = $

❐ $65 \times 65 = (___ \times _____) = (_____ \div _____) = $

❐ $75 \times 75 = (___ \times _____) = (_____ \div _____) = $

❐ $85 \times 85 = (___ \times _____) = (_____ \div _____) = $

❐ $95 \times 95 = (___ \times _____) = (_____ \div _____) = $

READ CAREFULLY

- Add 25 to the one's digit to get a sum having two digits.
- Write the square of the digits in the one's place as two digits.
- Write the square as two left-hand digits and the sum as two right-hand digits.

Find 50×50.

$0 + 25 = 25$ sum

$0 \times 0 = 00$ square

So 50×50

$= 2500$

DO YOURSELF

A. Find the squares mentally :

❏ 51×51 = $(1 + 25)$ = **26** and 1×1 = **01**. So 51×51 = 2601

❏ 52×52 = (___ + ___) = ___ and ___ × ___ = ___ =

❏ 53×53 = (___ + ___) = ___ and ___ × ___ = ___ =

❏ 54×54 = (___ + ___) = ___ and ___ × ___ = ___ =

❏ 55×55 = (___ + ___) = ___ and ___ × ___ = ___ =

❏ 56×56 = (___ + ___) = ___ and ___ × ___ = ___ =

❏ 57×57 = (___ + ___) = ___ and ___ × ___ = ___ =

❏ 58×58 = (___ + ___) = ___ and ___ × ___ = ___ =

❏ 59×59 = (___ + ___) = ___ and ___ × ___ = ___ =

58 VERTICES

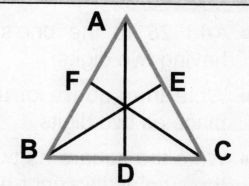

This triangle has three vertices A, B, C.
This triangle has three medians
AD, BE and CF.

DO YOURSELF

A. Name the **vertices** of each figure given below :

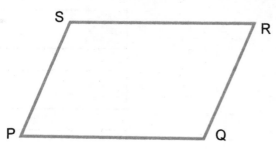

_____ , _____ , _____ , _____

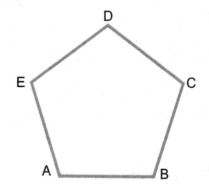

_____ , _____ , _____ , _____ , _____

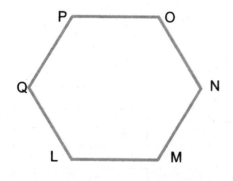

_____ , _____ , _____

_____ , _____ , _____

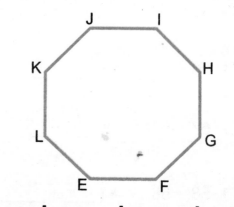

_____ , _____ , _____ , _____

_____ , _____ , _____ , _____

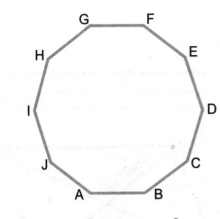

_____ , _____ , _____ , _____ , _____

_____ , _____ , _____ , _____ , _____

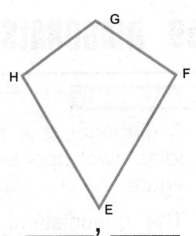

_____ , _____

_____ , _____

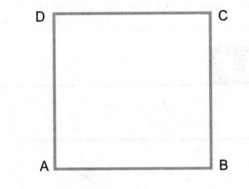

_____ , _____ , _____ , _____

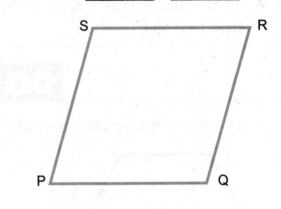

_____ , _____ , _____ , _____

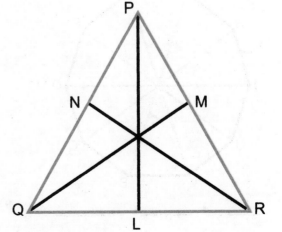

_____ , _____ , _____ , _____

Vertices : _____ , _____ , _____

Medians : _____ , _____ , _____

59 DIAGONALS

- A diagonal is a slanting line that joins two opposite vertices of a figure.

- The quadrilateral PQRS given in front has two diagonals PR and QS.

- The diagonals cut each other at the point O.

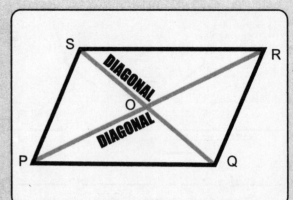

DO YOURSELF

A. Name the diagonals in each figure :

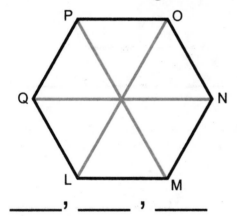

_____ , _____ , _____

_____ , _____

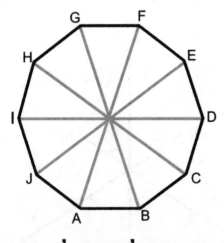

_____ , _____ , _____

_____ , _____

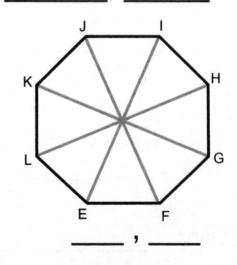

_____ , _____

_____ , _____

B. Draw the diagonals and name them :

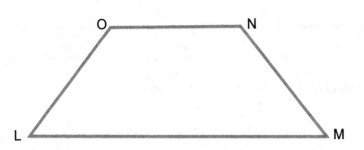

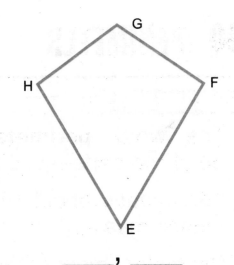

_____ , _____ ,

_____ , _____

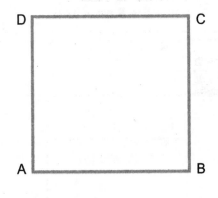

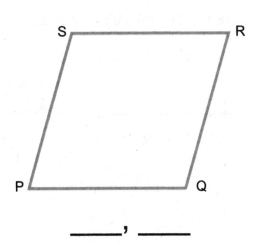

_____ , _____

_____ , _____

C. Fill up each blank :

1. A _____ means the angular point of a polygon.

2. A diagonal joins two opposite _____ of a figure.

3. A four-sided figure has _____ diagonals.

4. A median joins a vertex to the middle-point of the opposite ____ .

5. A _____ has 3 diagonals.

6. An octagon has _____ diagonals.

7. A _____ has five diagonals.

8. A trapezium has _____ diagonals.

9. A triangle has _____ medians.

60 PERIMETER

READ CAREFULLY

- The word—**perimeter**—is made up of two parts—peri and meter.

- Peri means about / round. Meter means measure.

- Perimeter means the boundary length of an enclosed figure.

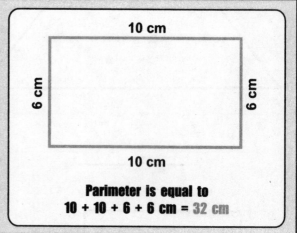

Parimeter is equal to
10 + 10 + 6 + 6 cm = 32 cm

DO YOURSELF

A. Find the **perimeter** of each figure given below :

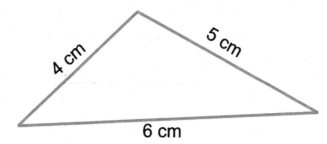

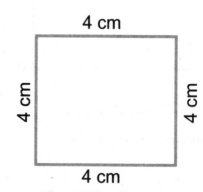

Perimeter = _____

Perimeter = _____

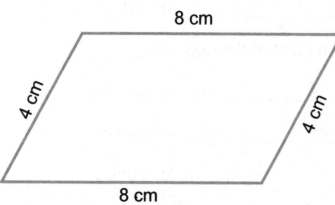

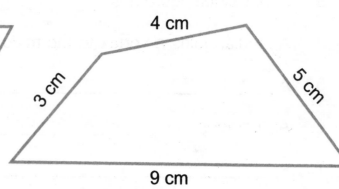

Perimeter = _____

Perimeter = _____

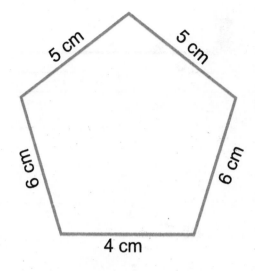

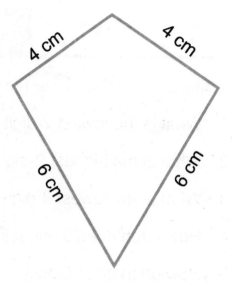

Perimeter = _____

Perimeter = _____

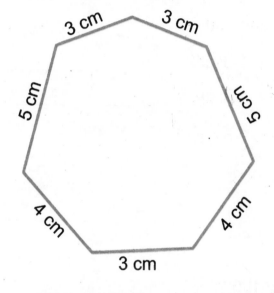

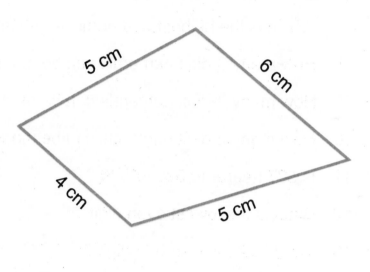

Perimeter = _____

Perimeter = _____

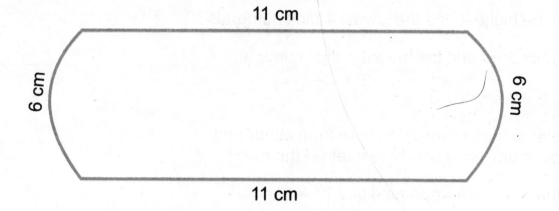

Perimeter = _____

A. Write the answer in each blank :

1. What is the lowest 2-digit numeral ?   10

2. What is the highest 2-digit numeral ?   99

3. What is the lowest 3-digit numeral ?   100

4. How often does 5 occur in the one's place from 5 to 95 ?   _____

5. How often does 5 occur in the ten's place from 50 to 59 ?   _____

6. Which is the highest even numeral between 1 and 100 ?   _____

7. Which is the highest odd numeral between 1 and 100 ?   _____

8. How many 3-digit numerals can be made using 1-digit ?   _____

9. How many 3-digit numerals can be made using 3-digits ?   _____

10. How many 2-digit numerals can be made using 2-digits ?   _____

11. Is 527 nearer to 520 or 530 ?   _____

12. What is the lowest even digit ?   _____

13. What is the lowest odd digit ?   _____

14. How many prime numerals are their from 1 to 100 ?   _____

15. Find the difference between :

   (*a*) the highest and the lowest 4-digit numerals :   _____

   (*b*) hundred and the lowest 3-digit numeral :   _____

   (*c*) 5 × 2 and 2 × 5 :   _____

16. Peter stands seventh in a row from either end.
     How many boys are there in all in the row ?   _____

17. What are the four prime digits ?

_____   _____   _____   _____